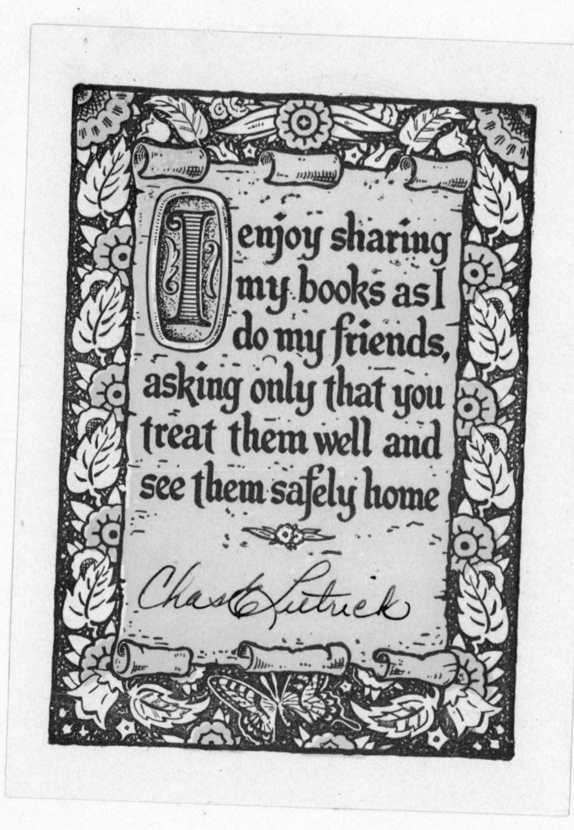
I enjoy sharing
my books as I
do my friends,
asking only that you
treat them well and
see them safely home
Chas E. Lutrick

The THEOLOGY *of* REINHOLD NIEBUHR

The THEOLOGY *of* REINHOLD NIEBUHR

by HANS HOFMANN
Translated by Louise Pettibone Smith

New York 1956
CHARLES SCRIBNER'S SONS

Printed in the United States of America

LIBRARY OF CONGRESS CATALOG CARD NO. 56-5663

Translator's Preface

The chief problem in a translation such as this is the recurring necessity of choice between precise reproduction of the original and the need for readability and clarity. The choice of the latter involved chiefly dividing the long complex sentences, with a consequent loss of unity; the omission or alteration of connectives, tending to over-simplification; and the avoidance of hyphenated compounds, with a loss of precision.

For the relation between God, man and society, a pivotal concept of the book, the writer used various terms. To convey with any precision the different shades of meaning of the German synonyms, compounds such as *God-man-frame-of-reference*, *the-state-of-existing-in-connection* and words like *co-inherence* and *co-involvement* would be needed. It seemed to the translator that such emphasis in English on minor differences tended to obscure a central theme of the book and the single term *relatedness* has been used throughout except where some particular qualification seemed essential to the context.

Sincere thanks are due to Professor George Riggan of the Hartford Seminary Foundation and to Miss Dorothea Harvey of the Department of Biblical History, Wellesley College, for their help in reading the translation and suggesting improvements. Since the suggestions were not always followed, the translator alone is to be blamed for the obscurities remaining.

LOUISE PETTIBONE SMITH

Professor of Biblical History, Emeritus, Wellesley College
Robert D. Campbell Visiting Professor of Religion,
Wells College, 1955–56

Contents

The THEOLOGY *of* REINHOLD NIEBUHR

I. Introduction

Niebuhr's whole theological burden grew from his surprise at the depth of the social problems he encountered as a young pastor in Detroit during and after the First World War. The changes which the assembly line introduced went far beyond the field of economics and radically affected the self-understanding of the worker and his relation to his environment. Niebuhr, equipped with the neat moralism of traditional liberalism, found himself absolutely unable to cope with the real problems of his congregation.

This led him, over the course of the years, to see that the problem of man is not to be solved merely by knowledge, progress, improvement or evolution. Man's problem is sin, in the full Biblical understanding of the word. With this foundation, Niebuhr was able to diagnose the troubles of the modern world as springing from, and in turn aggravating, man's unique predicament which expresses itself as sin.

The radical understanding of the problem then led him to look for a radical solution, and taking Christianity more seriously than did the majority of its advocates, he was brought to an appreciation of atonement and justification by faith, in their true Biblical relevance.

In order to do justice to this unusual and exciting development, we shall, with it in mind, look at his writings in their chronological order. Following that we shall correlate our findings in a more systematic way, on the plan indicated by Niebuhr himself in his more formally structured works, *The Nature and Destiny of Man* and *Faith and History*. This procedure calls for considerable verbatim quotation, especially since we are eager to have Niebuhr speak for himself, so that we may get an accurate and adequate portrayal of his thought.

One may not feel that he has spoken the final word in this field. One may not even agree with him at all. But no one can understand his own theological heritage, much less be in a position to transcend its shortcomings, if he disregards this decisive milestone on the way to an American theology.

This volume, originally published in Switzerland in 1954 under the title *Die Theologie Reinhold Niebuhrs, im Lichte seiner Lehre von der Sunde*, is based on research done at Princeton Theological Seminary and Union Theological Seminary during 1951–'52. To English-speaking readers, to whom Niebuhr's writings are directly available, it may serve as a systematic introduction to the principal ideas and the structure of the thought of this outstanding theologian. Two considerations seem to make such an introduction advisable.

First of all, Niebuhr's work is a unique attempt to relate genuine Christianity to the contemporary world by taking both equally seriously. This involves a keenly intuitive and incisive analysis of modern society and all its implications for human existence. No serious Christian, holding a position of responsibility in either the church or the secular order, can justify pursuing his work without taking into account Niebuhr's truly prophetic message.

Secondly, Niebuhr's own clarity of vision and synthesis, which is the fruit of his concern, background, and individual turn of mind, are not always evident in his works. It is often difficult to discover the motivation and implicit structure of some apparently unrelated remarks.

It is therefore the purpose of this volume to demonstrate the inner unity of Niebuhr's thought and thus to allow the reader to enjoy a more enlightening and fruitful study of Niebuhr's writings.

I am greatly indebted to Dr. Louise Pettibone Smith, who offered all her skill and experience in translating theological literature, and endless patience, to make this book available in English.

I am also deeply grateful to Charles Scribner's Sons, for their interest and cooperation in publishing this translation.

HANS HOFMANN

Princeton, N.J.
November, 1955

II. The Beginning

For Reinhold Niebuhr more than for any other contemporary theologian it is important to consider what determined the starting-point of his theological work in order to understand him. A knowledge of Niebuhr's beginning is important not solely because his later unique development becomes clear thereby, but because he has in fact never altered the essential direction of his searching and questioning. Whoever speaks of a change or a schism in Niebuhr's thinking must define precisely to what he refers. He must make it clear that although both self-consistency and change are found in Niebuhr's work, his one great concern remains always the same; the changes are confined to his theological or philosophical views.

In Niebuhr's endeavor to clarify and satisfy this concern, various attempts at clarification and solution have either proven pertinent and valuable or have been discarded as useless or even as misleading. Niebuhr is no intellectual dilettante who ties together without plan a variegated bouquet of carelessly gathered flowers of thought and observation. He is a man who from the beginning of his search for the solution of a fundamental question can neither be satisfied with an easy answer nor cease his effort until he finds what is to him the convincing and correct conclusion.

Starting from *a* question about man, he now demands *the* truth about man. Unweariedly he cons again and again the course of human events in order that he may see it ever more clearly; and that it may ultimately surrender the key to man's self-knowledge.

If the above is true, two results follow. First there must be in Reinhold Niebuhr's theology a single persistent concern, reciprocally related to all the other elements of his thinking in such a way that his work as a whole develops in conformity with it. And second, this concern must show itself especially clearly at the beginning where it is not yet involved with a multitude of considerations which arose during later controversies. If we desire then to begin at the actual beginning, we shall be wise to consider first Reinhold Niebuhr's starting-point.

In 1915 the minister's son, twenty-three years old, had finished his academic and seminary training and accepted the call of the small Evangelical and Reformed church in Detroit to be its pastor. He found himself faced with an exceedingly difficult task. He was set in the midst of the economic and social effects of the industrial metamorphosis which Henry Ford had brought to the city. The assembly line of mass production had not only engulfed the industry of yesterday which depended on individual skill; it had more and more demolished it. It was plain that this industrial transformation was changing and molding the life and character of the men absorbed into it.

Niebuhr must have had in mind from his theological training the picture of man as a religious individual whose interests were intellectual and spiritual and were not seriously affected by external economic and social factors. This was the image which satisfied the hearers and readers of the lectures delivered by Adolf von Harnack in 1900 on the nature of Christianity.* [1] Reinhold Niebuhr realized, thanks to the sensitive honesty and open-mindedness which are his especial characteristics, that the people of his parish did not resemble that picture, nor would they be influenced by it. He was therefore faced with a concrete decision. Should he continue in the established tradition, ignore

* *The notes, being chiefly source references, are found at the back of the book.*

the fundamental economic overturn which determined the lives of the members of his church, tend only the spiritual garden of personal edification, act "as if nothing were happening"? Or should he concern himself seriously with man in his actual existence, consider with brotherly love the conditions and difficulties of his life and seek to discover by searching together with him what the message of the Christian church has to say to him here and now in his actual situation? Here basically is the deepest purpose of the whole of Niebuhr's work. We rightly understand him only when we see that this decision was for him no problem.

The significant impact of Reinhold Niebuhr on American religious thought came precisely because he began to see, and saw ever more clearly, that preaching and pastoral care must be the expression of God's serious concern for man in his present concrete situation, and of God's love for him. The servants of God cannot evade sharing this concern unless they are willing to be wholly and entirely "unprofitable servants."

Of course, Walter Rauschenbusch had lived and worked before Niebuhr. But the movement of the so-called "Social Gospel" with its deep social concern was in some danger—if it did not entirely succumb—of narrowing the whole message of the Bible to an improved edition of the *Communist Manifesto;* of extracting out of the complete gospel to men in society a kind of socialized social gospel. In contrast, Niebuhr sought neither to escape from real life into a religious sanctuary nor to separate a single section of the Biblical message from the whole because of its apparent social applicability.

In 1920 the young pastor entered in his diary:

"I am really beginning to like the ministry. I think since I have stopped worrying so much about the intellectual problems of religion and have begun to explore some of its ethical problems there is more of a thrill in preaching. The real meaning of the gospel is in conflict with most of the customs and attitudes of our day at so many places that there is adventure in the Christian message, even if you only play around with its ideas in a conventional world.

I can't say that I have done anything in my life to dramatize the conflict between the gospel and the world. But I find it increasingly interesting to set the two in juxtaposition at least in my mind and in the minds of others. And of course ideas may finally lead to action." [2]

It is not only "the real meaning of the gospel" and still less is it simply "the customs and attitudes of our day" which occupied Niebuhr's thought. It was the fact that these are in conflict with each other on wide fronts. The young pastor felt himself propelled toward "adventure in the Christian message." And yet it was not pure search for adventure which drove him forth either to try to upset all conventional Christianity or to remake from A to Z the world which confronted him. "In my mind and in the minds of others" he begins cautiously "to bring the two into juxtaposition," and he adds significantly "and of course ideas may finally lead to action."

This method of procedure, which indeed distinguishes the true constructive reformer from the blind, ephemeral assailant and the visionary wrecker, precisely characterizes the development and marks the limits of Niebuhr's work as a whole. In consequence, those who expected from him primarily a systematic theological restoration and equally those who hoped from him a social revolution fitted to their taste will later be disappointed.

Niebuhr's starting-point needs even more precise characterization. He does not begin from an interest in any sort of "pure research," nor does he have any kind of program, theological or social, before him. His thinking never originates from a purely philosophical or theological outlook, and hence it can never be rightly or fully understood from such a perspective.[3] It originates wholly in the fundamental concern of the young pastor who found "more of a thrill in preaching" when he began "to explore the ethical problems" of religion. It must always be remembered—it will appear more and more clearly—that it is Niebuhr the preacher who finds himself in a very specific situation and environment and who then forces Niebuhr the thinker to explore the problems presented by that situation and to think them through to a helpful conclusion. It is therefore Niebuhr, preacher and shepherd of souls, who finds the point of attack for his whole theological and philosophical searching and questioning, and who extends from that beginning the channels of his thinking. It is not the reverse.

Niebuhr's dialectic, if a technical term of so many meanings can be used here at all to advantage, is never a philosophical presupposition, nor a fixed principle of thinking to which all knowledge must conform. Niebuhr's work would have to be cut to fit the Procrustean bed of a strict system and thereby much of the wealth of his thought excised or torn from its context and misinterpreted, as Carnell has done,[4] in order to find in it Hegel's thesis, antithesis, and synthesis; or to label Niebuhr as a strict follower of Kierkegaard.

Reinhold Niebuhr is related to the so-called dialectical theology of Europe much more in the content of his thought than in form or method. It cannot be denied that many important connecting lines lead from him to this theological movement of continental Europe. These would be worth specific and thorough investigation. There are similarities of beginnings also. As the leaders of dialectical theology in Europe had been aroused by the social-religious movement which preceded them, so was the young Niebuhr influenced by Walter Rauschenbusch.

But if we compare the assault made by young Barth in his commentary on Romans [5] with the first work of young Niebuhr, both agreement and difference will be sufficiently clear. The starting point is the same; for both, the relatedness of God and man has become the fundamental question. But Barth sees this relatedness so distorted and destroyed by the misconceptions of the theology of the preceding period that God can only be recognized by men as "the Wholly Other" who will always break into human existence only vertically—from above. On the other hand, the statement that "the real meaning of the gospel is in conflict with most of the customs and attitudes of our day at so many places" shows that for the young Niebuhr the question is primarily only of an impairing, through man himself, of the always existent and ever valid relation between man and God. Niebuhr sees his task therefore as first to learn the nature of the human impairment of the relatedness to God so that it can then be re-established and gospel and world can be brought into mutual relation. He expressly adds what the young Barth could never have said of himself, "I can't say that I have done anything in my life to dramatize the conflict between the gospel and the world." This difference of judgment upon a question equally fundamental to both has remained—at least seen from Niebuhr's side—unchanged until today.[6]

Niebuhr stands always precisely on the battle line between the gospel and human behavior. He never retreats to one of the two poles in order to examine from there and from there alone. If we wish to follow the course of his thought we must accompany him from front line to front line in the war between gospel and human action. And we shall be forced to admit that from the battleline he turns the light of criticism effectively both upon the proclamation of the gospel and upon the world to which it must be proclaimed. He attains a new understanding of both.

But it is not Niebuhr the systematic theologian who found use for the dialectic form of expression which emphasized the unrelated and unrelatable difference between God and man. It is always and especially Niebuhr the preacher and pastor who, recognizing the perversion by man of the real and ever persisting relatedness between man and God, centred his efforts concretely on restoring the true character of that relatedness.

His dialectic is therefore neither the evolutionary thought of pure idealism like Hegel's, nor an expression of the solely vertical relation between God and man, thinkable only from God's side, as by Barth. It is perhaps more akin to the dialectic of Kierkegaard, in which the two poles always keep a balance so that existence is actually insoluble and hopeless. But Niebuhr's dialectic in spite of an apparent similarity differs from Kierkegaard's decisively for with Niebuhr the dialectic is actually unreal. It has no actual original existence and it presses always toward a solution. For Niebuhr, dialectic statement has no Hegelian inevitability and no necessity of being. Nor does it, as with Barth, express an ultimate truth. It is merely a form of expression required by the perverted and unreal human view of God-man relatedness.

We see then that there is no approach to Niebuhr from the outside. He must be understood directly from his own position. Therefore we shall now listen to what he himself says in a look backward at his own development.

"The only biographical note which I can add, in conclusion is that such theological convictions which I hold today began to dawn upon me during the end of a pastorate in a great industrial city. They dawned upon me because the simple little moral homilies which were preached in that as in other cities, by myself and others, seemed completely irrelevant to the brutal facts of life in a great industrial center. Whether irrelevant or not, they were certainly futile. They did not change human actions or attitudes in any problem of collective behavior by a hair's breadth, though they may well have helped to preserve private amenities and to assuage individual frustration.

"These convictions which dawned in my pastorate have been further elaborated in a teaching position in a theological seminary. Greater leisure has given me opportunity to discover the main currents and emphases of the classical ages of Christian thought, and to find insights there which have been long neglected and which are yet absolutely essential to modern man, or indeed to man of any age.

"However, since I am not so much scholar as preacher, I must confess that the gradual unfolding of my theological ideas has come not so much through study as through the pressure of world events. Whatever measure of Christian faith I hold today is due to the gradual exclusion of alternative beliefs through world history. As did Peter, I would preface my confession 'Thou hast words of eternal life,' with the question, 'Lord, to whom shall we go?' Even while imagining myself to be preaching the gospel, I had really experimented with many alternatives to Christian faith, until one by one they proved unavailing." [7]

It is true then not only of the beginning but of the whole of Niebuhr's life work, that he is the preacher—not the scholar interested in research for its own sake, and still less the pure apologist. He has tested the various world systems of belief which oppose the gospel either implicitly or consciously and explicitly. He has examined them from the point of view of the gospel, not in order to cast them easily aside but that he may understand them in their historical setting and so evaluate their immanent and temporal significance. But precisely thereby he is enabled to repudiate their hidden or open claim to be ways of faith which provide the possibility of redemption from our historical enslavement, and so to be rivals of the gospel.

Because Niebuhr remains faithful to this method of work which was the consequence of his point of departure, we shall expect from him no theological system. We must not measure him unfairly against one or another of the earlier or contemporary systems of theology, for in so doing we should misunderstand and diminish his real contribution.

Nor shall we consider him as a philosopher, nor as a sociological analyst who would offer us so-called objective, scientific knowledge. We shall always remember that Reinhold Niebuhr is the preacher who stands on the line of battle between gospel and world, who is seriously concerned with the world and observes it scientifically; but who tests equally rigorously the message of the gospel. So he demonstrates that the gospel message never loses sight of the real world.

The relation of gospel and world to each other is the main theme of Niebuhr's work. His starting-point is the conflict between them which results from the disturbance and rupture of their relation—from what the Bible calls sin. His concern is the proclamation of the re-establishment of the relation—of what in the Bible is called grace. Through his own experience in preaching he knows that all effort becomes detached and unfruitful if either pole of this relation is excluded. He has learned that "the simple little moral homilies" are irrelevant if they are not related to "the brutal facts of life." But he also acknowledges "the gradual exclusion of alternative beliefs through world history." He has never left the battlefield in order to find rest in monism at one of the two poles. He observed indeed in the history of theology retreats in both directions, but he saw most clearly that in such retreats sin was never seriously enough regarded. He himself therefore applied himself steadily to the exploration of the area of conflict.

We are therefore confident that we are not taking a wrong position when we, in what follows, direct our attention chiefly to Niebuhr's understanding of sin. Rather, we can expect to find here his most significant pronouncements on world and gospel. From here we should be best able to make clear the fundamental structure of his thought and its far-reaching implications.

III. Religion and Society

A. Religion and Society: A Question Directed to Religion

We stated earlier that Niebuhr took his stand intentionally on the battleline between gospel and world. His first book with its provocative title *Does Civilization Need Religion?* [1] attacks the question with a certain slant against religion. The author seeks to explore the front line by radically challenging religion itself. He is not willing to abandon any part of human existence as a foggy no-man's land between the fronts. It is necessary to see clearly not only where religion can stand strong and in its own right, but also where society stands with its own rights and duties.

Niebuhr then begins his investigation at once with a very pessimistic prognosis of the prospects of religion in modern society. Modern science and the development of the modern economy have mightily increased the difficulties of religion, and religion on its side has shown itself almost incapable of meeting these difficulties. Niebuhr turns first therefore to a critical consideration of religion and declares:

"A psychology of defeat, of which both fundamentalism and modernism are symptoms, has gripped the forces of religion. Extreme orthodoxy betrays by its very frenzy that the poison of scepticism has entered the soul of the church; for men insist most vehemently upon their certainties when their hold upon them has been shaken. Frantic orthodoxy is a method for obscuring doubt. Liberalism tries vainly to give each new strategic retreat the semblance of a victorious engagement. . . . There are indeed many forms of religion which are clearly vestigial remnants of another day with other interests. They have no vital influence upon the life of modern man, and their continued existence only proves that history, like nature, is slow to destroy what it has found useless, and even slower to inter what it has destroyed. Scattered among the living forms of each civilization are the whitened bones of what was once flesh and blood." [2]

So from the very beginning Niebuhr makes his purpose entirely clear. Although his liberal theological training unquestionably influenced him in more than mere terminology, he is plainly not concerned with criticizing one theological camp from the position of the other. In both he sees symptoms of "a psychology of defeat"; whether the occupants of one camp "rage" in "frenzy" or those in the other give their "strategic retreats the semblance of a victorious engagement," both show equally in their frantic self-justification that in wide areas they lack vital force and significance. He begins then by presenting an astounding picture of the natural decay which always occurs whenever the forces of life have receded from worn-out forms. This metaphor, which we shall encounter often, shows significantly that Niebuhr is thinking in almost the terms of naturalistic dynamism. Even religion is not excepted, but seems to him subject to a law of life superior to it. One is almost tempted to label him a radical Naturalist or even a Utilitarian when we read his reply to a question concerning this law above religion:

"If religion contains indispensible resources for the life of man, its revival waits only upon the elimination of those maladjustments which have hindered it from making its resources available for the citizen of the modern era." [3]

But we misunderstand Niebuhr if we forget what was said earlier: that he is concerned with making clear the line of battle between gospel and world, and that religion for him is not just an immanent human possibility. Its present local and transient manifestation is only a kind of spring-house erected over the ever-flowing spring which "contains indispensible resources for the life of man." Solely because it is important to keep uncluttered the spring-house beneath which the sources of religion rise, human institutions erected yesterday to conform to yesterday's patterns must be torn down, since today "maladjustments" have prevented making the source itself "available for the citizen of the modern era."

In what follows, it will be necessary to scrutinize carefully what Niebuhr seems to be saying about the concept, *religion;* to note whether he is speaking of the source itself or of the human and therefore censurable structure of the spring-house. It is clear that the source of religion in its immediate and unconditioned relation to men remains for him above criticism.

In fact, it is from this unconditioned relation that the criterion is won by which all religions are judged as human attempts to create this relation. Niebuhr makes this clear when he writes:

"Whatever may be said of specific religions and religious forms, it is difficult to imagine man without religion; for religion is the champion of personality in a seemingly impersonalized world. It prompts man to organize his various impulses, inherited and acquired, into a moral unity; it persuades him, when its vitality is unimpaired, to regard his fellows with an appreciation commensurate with his own self-respect; and it finally discovers and creates a universe in which the human spirit is guaranteed security against the forces of nature which always seem to reduce it to a mere effervescence unable to outlast the collocation of forces which produced it. The plight of religion in our own day is due to the fact that it has been more than ordinarily pressed by foes on the two lines on which it defends the dignity and value of personality. The sciences have greatly complicated the problem of maintaining the plausibility of the personalization of the universe by which religion guarantees the worth of human personality; and science applied to the world's work has created a type of society in which personality is easily debased." [4]

It is easy to understand that Niebuhr under the still fresh impact of Detroit's assembly-line technique sees the salvation of society in free and independent human personalities. The character of such a personality is conceived neither idealistically nor naturalistically, but as socially conditioned, as "[regarding] his fellows with an appreciation commensurate with his own self-respect." Personality is a requisite for society. It never has meaning and purpose in itself, but only as it makes possible an integrated and responsible society.

"Personality is that type of reality which is self-conscious and self-determining. The concept of personality is valid only in a universe in which creative freedom is developed and maintained in individual life as well as in the universe." [5]

The Naturalism of the natural sciences is therefore discarded because it prevents the individual from becoming a person and so prevents an integrated society. Because the cosmos is detached from any relation to a personal creator and has become an irresponsible machine, the impersonality of nature has depersonalized society. Niebuhr sees a connecting arch, reaching from God to a society of persons in a universe personally determined—an arch built of individual men, with religion as its builder. Religion in the highest sense is portrayed by the necessity of conjoining the two piers of the arch if the structure is to endure.

"It [religion] teaches men to find God by loving their brothers and to love their brothers because they have found God. It inspires a mystical reverence for human personality, prompted by the discovery and creation of a universe in which personality is the supreme power and value; and it persuades men to discover personal values in the universe because they have first come upon clues to the transcendent value of personality in the lives of their fellows." [6]

Religion, fighting for personality on two fronts, on the one against the Naturalism which depersonalizes the universe and nature, on the other against a civilization which depersonalizes society, is in danger from two sides in two different areas, both essential.

"Religion is thus obviously placed in a desperate plight when its metaphysics and its ethics are imperiled at the same time. It must face and do battle with two hosts of enemies, those who do not believe in men because they do not believe in God, and those who do not believe in God because modern civilization has robbed them of their faith in the moral integrity of men." [7]

Niebuhr wishes above all else to make clear how absolutely indispensible is the relation between God and society if the structure of human society is to endure. God alone makes possible a sound society in which conversely true faith in God can live and operate effectively. The preservation and renewal of this relatedness to God is the increasingly difficult task of religion. Here the main theme of Niebuhr's whole theology is sounded. It can be briefly stated: religion through the living relation to God creates in man intelligent persistence in his unique function of mediation; this function produces the essence of personality and through it society first becomes a possibility.

But because it is difficult to solve two problems at once, to contend for the personality of God which is necessary to make possible a world of persons, and for the personal society necessary to make possible the preservation of a personal faith in God, religion has usually chosen to contend for one only, and that the easier.

"It is easier to challenge the idea of an impersonal universe than to change the fact of an impersonal civilization." [8]

Religion expends all its energy on the metaphysical front against a deterministic science; and consequently the other, the ethical front, is neglected. It is this ethical front, however, which Niebuhr sees as predominately urgent and significant.

"In the present situation of religion in civilization, it is more necessary to inquire if and how the peculiar attitudes and the unique life which proceeds from a religious interpretation of the universe may be made to serve the needs of men in modern civilization. The fact is that more men in our modern era are irreligious because religion has failed to make civilization ethical than because it has failed to maintain its intellectual respectability. For every person who disavows religion because some ancient and unrevised dogma outrages his intelligence, several become irreligious because the social impotence of religion outrages their conscience." [9]

Niebuhr would certainly not separate completely the two tasks of religion which he sees and devote himself to one only, but he views religion as gravely suspect when it confines itself to the easier but less urgent task of the intellectual battle against deterministic Naturalism. For himself he sees the greater exigency and the main responsibility in the area where God and society must be and can be immediately related if society, personalized, will recognize its ethical responsibility before the personal God.

But now the question is, how and where will this happen. We shall at first be somewhat astonished when Niebuhr answers:

"The value of religion in composing the conflict with which the inner man is torn is that it identifies man's highest values, about which he would center his life, with realities in the universe itself, and teaches him how to bring his momentary impulses under the domination of his will by subjecting his will to the guidance of an absolute will." [10]

Here with few words Niebuhr teaches us that we are wrong if we look for the solution of the social and ethical question somewhere outside of ourselves, in society and its organization. The rift which divides the whole world, does not cease at man, but divides and disintegrates him also. Actually it originates in him. This most important fact, to which psychiatry bears clear witness, makes it forever impossible for us to postulate man as the sure and permanent foundation for the rebuilding of society. On the contrary, the problem of the integration of human personality is basic and critical for the solution of all the remaining problems. But a solution for the primary problem cannot be found if it is isolated from the other problems; nor if we seek to centre human personality in itself. A solution can be found only when personality is centred in the higher value "by subjecting man's will to the guidance of an absolute will." The integration of personality is not an isolated and independent problem any more than are the other problems—it also is a question of relatedness. Personality can become integrated only within a community and into a community; only within and into world relatedness. Just so far as it transcends itself is it fulfilled.

Consequently, two opposite but similar movements are recognizable. On the one hand is the vitiation of the relatedness of God and man, and with it of religion; on the other hand, the destruction of the relation of man and society, and with it, as society itself testifies, the disintegration of man himself, the mediator of the double relatedness. But the problem of man himself, of the healing of his personal disintegration, obtrudes itself again in reverse by its effect on the relation between God and religion and on man's associations with his fellows in society.

This inter-relatedness is at first important for Niebuhr primarily because if its social consequences—later with a different significance it becomes central in his thinking. The socializing of men and the humanizing of society are not merely closely connected converses. They are both equally closely connected with the problem of extending the relatedness of society beyond men to the universe and finally beyond the universe to the personal will of God, creator and sustainer of the universe. Only so does man find his place in the communion of the cosmos which is personally ordered by the highest will. For men, vertical and horizontal relatedness belong inseparably together and together solve the problem of man's own personal integration.

But Niebuhr rightly warns against unconsciously assuming that one of the two problems is already solved, and consequently neglecting it.

"Obviously the function of religion in the life of the individual has its social implications; but it is not to be assumed that the integration of personality automatically solves man's social problems. That assumption, which religion invariably makes, is one of its very defects in dealing with the social problem. A unified personality may still be anti-social in its dominant desires and the very self-respect which issues from its higher integration may become the screen for its unsocial attitudes.

"Just as important as the problem of bringing peace to the warring factions within the soul of man is the task of giving human personality a sense of worth in the face of nature's indifference and contempt; and of adjusting man's highest values to nature's sublimer moods." [11]

Because religion is often enough in danger of going wrong in the treatment of social problems by assuming that their solution is an automatic result of the integration of personality, Niebuhr intentionally sets himself as a corrective on the other side, and speaks often and forcibly of the relatedness of man and society.

"The question which we really face, therefore, is whether religion is constitutionally but a sublimation of man's will to live or whether it can really qualify the will of the individual and restrain his expansive desires for the sake of society." [12]

He now inquires earnestly and critically concerning the social forces of religion and refuses to be content with any sentimental, or superficial, or unworkable assertions. The social force of religion he finds chiefly in the fact that:

"it [religion] persuades men to regard their fellows as their brothers because they are all children of God. It insists, in other words, that temporal circumstance and obvious differences are dwarfed before the spiritual affinities which men have through their common relation to a divine creator." [13]

But this judgment does not lead him into a shallow idealism.

"Yet understanding alone does not solve all the problems of living together. We do not hate only those whom we do not know or understand. Sometimes we hate those most whom we know best. Love does not flow inevitably out of intimacy. Intimacy may merely accentuate previous attitudes, whether they be benevolent or malevolent." [14]

"Even if intelligence became imaginative enough to discover the affinities, it could not be courageous enough to challenge the evil in men in the name of their better selves. The art of forgiveness can be learned only in the school of religion. And it is an art which men must learn increasingly as a complex society makes human associations more and more intimate." [15]

"In its highest form religion does inculcate a wholesome spirit of humility which gives the soul no peace in any virtue while higher virtue is attainable." [16]

"Humility is therefore a spiritual grace which has value not only for its own sake but for its influence upon social problems.

"Traditional religions, which live off of original inspirations and experiences without recreating them, easily fall into a pride of their own, the pride which comes from identifying the absolute standards of their inspired source with their partial achievements and inevitable compromises. But religion in its purest and most unspoiled form is always productive of a spirit of humility which regards every moral achievement as but a vantage point from which new ventures of faith and life are to be initiated toward the alluring perfection which is in God." [17]

Again a note is sounded which will lead further and is later to become definitive. In *humility* Niebuhr sees a primary effect, perhaps the decisive effect of religion. Humility, conferred by the source of religion, presages man's mounting renewal and progress. It frees man from the self-seeking egotism which keeps him in isolated self-relatedness and results in manifold injuries to his personality, hinders his effectiveness in society, and worst of all makes impossible man's true function as mediator of the relatedness between God and the society of men in the world.

Here we need to note especially the use of the term *religion.* It is significant for the early Niebuhr that intentionally he writes of religion and not of Christianity. In accordance with the liberal tradition, he sees in Christianity only a particular manifestation of universal religiousness, which appears among other universal human phenomena. Later we shall consider at what point and for what reasons Niebuhr revised this conception of religion until, with his new understanding of revelation, the word *religion* almost vanishes from his vocabulary. In the present context, it is important to recognize that the starting-point for such a change is already given in the clear distinction between "the resources of religion" and "the traditional religions." For the phrase "resources of religion" recognizes that something which comes from outside man acts on man, and that this something makes possible and sustains man's religiousness. Such a recognition already points towards the doctrine of revelation.

Niebuhr, in a way which reminds us of the "ad fontes" of the Reformation, emphasizes the fresh and dynamic activity which is continually flowing from the "resources of religion." By it men are led to regard with humility all their undertakings, which, however well-intentioned at the beginning, are inevitably involved in compromise and end in encasing, restricting and stultifying the once living and active power. Men are forced to acknowledge all they do as incomplete and under judgment. By this "spiritual gift" of humility men are freed from themselves and from their own acquisitiveness and are enabled to undertake new tasks of social living in community. The force, constantly renewed from the source of religion, can never be ignored or dispensed with in meeting the ever-new problems of social life in the community, since it alone makes an adequate solution possible.

The guilt of the traditional religions, like the sin of religious men, consists in the desire for absolute independence and autonomy (which would of course make mediation impossible), the refusal to act as the humble servant, ever ready for new beginnings in mediating the relatedness of God to society. Men, instead of serving in the dynamic interaction of God and human society, erect a permanent and circumscribed institution, smugly absolutizing their own achievements and overlooking entirely the many compromises which made these achievements possible and limited their scope. It is tempting to cite the Roman Catholic Church as a striking example, but this might distract attention from the failures of Protestantism.

Niebuhr in fact assails the over-valuing of all institutional churches. He does not ignore the fact that they have their value as starting points, but a starting point must always be left behind and transcended. He does not attack seriatim every church form and institution—that would be fanatical stupidity—but he wholly repudiates the traditional religions which "live off of original inspirations and experiences without recreating them." The result is pride, the arrogant repudiation of the obligation of service in mediating the relatedness between God and society. Again we must remind ourselves that such repudiation corresponds precisely with what the Bible calls sin, for which the house of Israel was most sharply condemned.

"Religion is easily tempted to make devotion to the ideal a substitute for its realization and to become oblivious to the inevitable compromise between its ideal and the brute facts of life." [18]

It is noteworthy that Niebuhr does not consider compromise as objectionable in itself. It can very well be the manger in which the relatedness of God and man may be found, the place where the dynamic action of God through men in society becomes manifest in society. It can therefore be a way of making this relatedness actual. Niebuhr objects only to our forgetting that man makes such compromises because of his own shortcomings, and is always in danger of perverting and destroying every relation which he shares. This is not because man in himself or compromise in itself is essentially evil, but because man is always tempted to a self-willed over-riding of his own limitations. By this self-will he destroys his proper function of mediating the relatedness of God to society, and makes impossible his own true and fitting transcendence. The practical result of this dangerous behavior shows itself in the social conservatism of modern religions.

"The question which faces the modern church is whether it will help to hide or to discover the limitations in the ethical orientation of modern life." [19]

"It is obvious that the ethical potency of religion depends largely upon its ability to make its ideals effective in the world and yet preserve a measure of detachment from those natural forces which express themselves in human society and offer such stubborn resistance to every spiritual and ethical ideal that no victory has yet been gained over them in which the heel of the victor has not been bruised." [20]

"It was probably inevitable that the church should adjust the spiritual ideal, which to propagate it ostensibly regards as its very raison d'etre, to the practical needs of the various ages and social orders with which it came in contact. But it is necessary that it should be shrewd enough to see the compromise involved in every adjustment and be stubborn enough to make a new bid for victory after every partial defeat." [21]

But in criticizing the religious behavior of men in their function of mediating between God and society, we must not forget that this task has become exceedingly difficult in the society of today.

"Civilization has increased the size of groups in which human relations have an ethical basis, but it has not moralized the action of the group nor taught individuals in one social group to treat individuals in other groups with the respect and confidence which a wholesome social life requires." [22]

Whether we speak of society, or of man, or of men in society, we must recognize that the difficulties which an individual encounters in his contacts with society are still greater when the relations of whole groups of men to one another are in question. Although, or rather because, it is true that

"on the whole the unethical character of group action is determined as much by the partial virtues as by the vices of the individuals," [23] we must realize that "human imagination and intelligence have not been equal to the task of extending ethical attitudes beyond the boundaries of the group." [24]

If we now consider as a whole all that has been said, we must conclude that at the place of contact and conflict where God wills to manifest His relatedness to society, man has a two-fold task—not two different tasks, but one task which presents itself under two different aspects. On the one hand he should free himself from a false detachment from the world, a detachment rooted in the desire to preserve his own comfortable security by shunning all conflict. On the other hand he must so relate himself to the world that the world may be renewed by his mediation.

"The tendency of modern religion to make itself at home in the world and to enter into intimate relations with civilization is not due solely to the puritan confidence of victory over life. It is partly due to the influence of a sentimental and optimistic evaluation of human nature which came to the modern church through Rousseau and romanticism. It is also a product of the evolutionary optimism which has characterized religious thought since ethicists and religionists have learnt to overcome the melancholy conclusions implicit in the Darwinian theory and to see the bright side of evolution. Traditional religion is other-worldly. The modern church prides itself on its bright and happy worldliness. It is more interested in transforming the natural and social environment of personality than in persuading the soul to transcend all circumstances and find its happiness in inner peace. The modern church regards this mundane interest as its social passion. But it is also the mark of its slavery to society. Whenever religion feels completely at home in the world, it is the salt which has lost its savor. If it sacrifices the strategy of renouncing the world, it has no strategy by which it may convict the world of sin. A movement which detaches religion from life to give it a perspective and power over life must on the other hand run the risk of centering the interests of men on other than social problems. Religion thus faces a dilemma which is not easily solved. A religion of social amelioration easily becomes a beautiful romance which obscures the unlovely realities of life. A religion of detachment from the world may persuade the soul to find both happiness and virtue in defiance of physical and social circumstances and thus to regard all social problems as irrelevant to its main purpose. This dilemma is not due to any specific or historic weaknesses in types of religion but arises out of the nature and constitution of religion as such." [25]

Niebuhr here sees religion as the medium of man's relation with God, and therefore as necessarily an impediment to his complete identification with the world. Significantly he presents identification with the world and its antithesis, escape from the world, as opposite but equally illegitimate temptations of religion. Both must be avoided. (He equates them at times with the emphasis of Calvinism and of Lutheranism respectively.) But equally neither of them can be wholly escaped. According to Niebuhr, the religious problem of man is essentially the problem of true relatedness to God and to the world. Only in a true balance of the relation to God and the world is true religion possible. World-identification and world-escape put an intolerable over-weight upon one side of the balance or the other, under which the relation itself must break.

Basically, however, the danger of over-emphasis points to a necessary and legitimate concern. On the one hand, to be able to accomplish for the world the service of continual renewal, we must guard our distance from the world, not only that we may view the situation as a whole but also that we may avoid losing ourselves in a given situation by absolutizing it. On the other hand, the success of our service in the world is possible only if we accept with full responsibility our existence in the world as our assigned station for fulfilling our task. Niebuhr clearly has in mind the Johannine "in the world" but "not of the world." Both the *in* and the *not of* must be understood and accepted in its true meaning, without over-emphasizing either to the point of absurdity.

In Niebuhr's repudiation of one-sided emphasis, we again encounter the Biblical concept of sin. As he interprets it, full identification with the world results in separation from the sources of religion and finally from God Himself, but a complete escape from the world shows that we have either not understood or have not obeyed God's will that we work in the world. The two aspects of man's obligation to God and to society are closely related and neither can be fulfilled apart from the other. Total inter-relatedness is essential.

"The conclusion which emerges from such reflections will shock orthodox religionists. It is that the values of religion are conditioned and not absolute and that they attain their highest usefulness not when they subdue all other values but when they are in perpetual conflict with them, or it may be truer to say when they are cöordinated with them." [26]

"The cöordination is not easy because men are not inclined to be at once critical and appreciative of the values with which they must deal. They always tend to increase the limitations of certain values by an uncritical devotion, or to destroy the values in mad resentment against their limitations. Since man is a citizen of two worlds, he cannot afford to renounce his citizenship in either. He must work out his destiny as a child of nature and as a servant of the absolute." [27]

The two temptations of world-identification and world-escape, the temptation to deny citizenship and responsibility in one of the two worlds, may be called in theological terminology "monistic tendencies." They seek to by-pass dualistic polarity. Man is trying to justify and maintain the exclusion of one of the two poles of his existence. In opposition, Niebuhr resolutely affirms dualism. We have the right to refuse to be content with his affirmation, to question whether dualism is really a solution. We may even deny that it offers an approach to solving the problem and we may debate which of Niebuhr's "poles" would be the correct and only possible alternative to the other. Later we shall try to resolve these doubts.

But first we must allow Niebuhr to demonstrate that he has good and valid grounds for his decision.

"The only fruitful alternative to a monism and pantheism which identifies God and the world, the real and the ideal, is a dualism which maintains some kind of distinction between them and does not lose one in the other." [28]

"Early Hebrew religion was naïvely dualistic, and that is one reason why it has been so potent in the history of religion." [29]

In this connection it is important to realize that the monotheistic concern in the Old Testament led from an early, zealous monism to a clear dualism. The dualism manifested itself at the problem of evil, a fact which is very significant and which should give pause to both monism and pantheism.

"The Genesis account of the fall solves the problem of evil upon an essentially monistic basis by making human sin responsible for even the inadequacies of nature and attributing everything from weeds to mortality to the luckless error of the first man. Neither the goodness nor the omnipotence of God is abridged in this naïve but sublime conception in which the human conscience assumes responsibility for more than its share of human ills in order to save the reputation of divine virtue. . . . A profounder instinct than reveals itself to the casual observer persuades fundamentalism to defend the reality of the devil with such vehemence. It may be metaphysically inconsistent to have two absolutes, one good and one evil, but the conception provides at least for a dramatic portrayal of the conflict which disturbs the harmonies and unities of the universe, and therefore, it has a practical and ethical value. The idea of attributing personality to evil may be scientifically absurd but it rests upon a natural error. When the blind and impersonal forces of nature come to life in man they are given the semblance of personality." [30]

It is precisely adherence to the unity of God, maintained in spite of the problem of evil, which requires dualism. The men of the Bible were confronted by evil as a fact which could not be eliminated by theoretical speculations, and as a reality which was so active and powerful that it could easily be personified. If they had not nevertheless found it unthinkable that the good God could, in a sort of schizoid personality split, produce evil, there would have been no need for dualism. Behind the question of Monism, or Pantheism, or Dualism lies the much deeper question of the essence of God, which becomes the more urgent the more seriously we take the Biblical message of the self-revealing God. If we can truthfully assert that we believe in an absolutely good God, and do not feel ourselves oppressed by the restraints of Monism or Pantheism, it is because we are forcing ourselves to the stupidity of refusing to recognize the reality of evil.

For a consideration of Niebuhr's theology, it is especially important to realize how the problem of dualism obtrudes itself upon him at exactly this point in this specific fashion. He does not meet it on the philosophic plane of the problem of Good and Evil as related to each other; rather he makes plain, by connecting it directly with the Genesis narrative of the Fall, that dualism for him means the opposition between the good God who reveals Himself as such, and the sin of men.

The field of battle does not lie between the good man and the evil which threatens him, but between the good God and men who provide lodging for evil, the sinners. Dualism is therefore required, for it alone adequately expresses the actuality of the broken bond between God and man, and acknowledges the destruction by man himself of his relatedness to God and consequently also the destruction of his relatedness to his environment and ultimately of himself. Niebuhr emphasizes this dualism because, contrary to all monistic theories, the sin of man is so recognized for what it is—the breaking of man's relatedness to God and fellowmen, a relatedness which man might preserve but which can never be re-created by man. Dualism is neither necessary nor even possible in God, or from God's side. But it is equally impossible for man to extricate himself from dualism. Every such attempt creates dishonesty, where repentant humility is called for; and produces the monstrosity of man's sinful desire to save himself.

It is at this point that the person and the significance of Jesus emerge.

"In the early Christian church the naïve dualism of Jesus was given dramatic and dynamic force through his deification, so that he became, in a sense, the God of the ideal, the symbol of the redemptive force in life which is in conflict with evil." [31]

A specific assertion of dualism of exactly the kind indicated is evidently required.

"Its [early Christianity's] symbols lacked philosophical precision but they did give vivid and dramatic force to the idea of a conflict between evil and the redemptive and creative force in life. Thus it could fulfill the two great functions of religion in prompting men to repent of their sins, and in encouraging them to hope for redemption from them. No mechanical or magical explanations of the crucifixion have ever permanently obscured the helpful spiritual symbolism of the cross in which the conflict between good and evil is portrayed and the possibility as well as the difficulty of the triumph of the good over evil is dramatized. An absolute dualism either between God and the universe or between man and nature, or spirit and matter, or good and evil, is neither possible nor necessary." [32]

To Niebuhr, right evaluation of the problem of sin is the decisive criterion of the value of religion, and the fundamental weakness of modern religion, as he has come to realize, lies just here.

"Renouncing the idea of total depravity which was central in medieval religion, and in orthodox Protestantism for that matter, [Romanticism] evolved a sentimental over-estimate of human virtue which is no nearer the truth than the medieval conceptions of original sin." [33]

"The perennial conflict between priest and prophet is given in the double function of religion. The priest dispenses comfort and the prophet makes the challenge of religion potent. The priest is more numerous than the prophet because human selfishness is as determining in religion as in other fields. Though the priest always defeats the prophet in the end, the prophet is avenged because his original experience is the reality which makes the priest's assurance plausible." [34]

Niebuhr believes that both religious and secular thinking have, since the days of the Renaissance, exchanged their fundamental attitudes toward the world. The false optimism adopted by religion is now counterbalanced by the modest, even despairing realization of the "secular idealists." Which view is the more correct is less important for Niebuhr than the fact that modern religion no longer comprehends the insights of its own past and tosses them carelessly overboard even though they would give valuable enlightenment today.

The strident actualities of daily living, which challenge radically all attempts to give meaning to life, forced Niebuhr, in his desire to bring the gospel and the world into mutual relation, to forsake the current, wholly irrelevant and impotent theology in which he had been trained and to study seriously the theology of the past. He began this study, not out of theological curiosity or zeal for pure research, but to gain "more ethical force in preaching" so that the world might better know itself and therefore might change.

What first impressed him was, significantly, the old and apparently long buried doctrine of original sin. It is striking that Niebuhr, standing on the battle front between gospel and world, and believing that only when man knows himself as the link between God and society can man rightly understand himself, was led by the realities of the world and their interpretation by secular idealists to just this position. For him, religion today first becomes really modern when it reverts to this old insight of the fathers. Then only can it meet the demands of modern science and counter its claims.

But this requires that religion change. And for a religion which is in process of changing in order to meet new situations, the significant man is the prophet. What is to follow, therefore, applies to the prophet and to prophetic religion.

We have given particular attention to the ideas in this first book of Reinhold Niebuhr because we could there see clearly from what facts and from what questions Niebuhr proceeds. He began by seeking and inquiring, by clearing the ground. The book is a book of questioning and search. To require in it clear answers and fully articulated conclusions is unreasonable and unrewarding. It made its impact in America precisely because of its honest and frank questioning, its challenging of what was commonly accepted as self-evident.

Certainly it would be as useless as it would be easy to expend some systematizing acuteness in calling attention to the particular contradictions in the separate lines of Niebuhr's thought. They exist because he has not yet ventured to draw all the conclusions resulting from the insight which forced him to ask his questions. Twelve years later, he himself wrote of the book:

"I wrote a book, my first, in 1927 which when now consulted is proved to contain almost all the theological windmills against which today I tilt my sword. These windmills must have tumbled shortly thereafter for every succeeding volume expresses a more and more explicit revolt against what is usually known as liberal culture." [35]

That is certainly true, and Niebuhr's front line becomes ever more clearly defined. But for us who do not so much seek answers as desire to understand the questions, this book has especial value. It has shown us that Niebuhr was explicitly trying to investigate without prejudices or restrictions the place where gospel and world meet, and even more seriously trying to learn where first they can come into right relation. The search led him from the resources of religion through its human institutional embodiment to man and beyond man to the whole of human society, the whole world.

Right relatedness can preserve in living freshness and power the vital force of the sources of religion, enabling it not only to survive the changes of the times, but to give men guidance toward the goal. However, this relatedness has been seriously disturbed if not destroyed because man became tired of his role as mediating link and desired to take the ordering of events into his own hands. So to insure himself against unpleasant surprises from the sources of religion, he remodeled the spring-house into a dam and stopped the flow from the source. But the water which he had desired to bring under his own control has become stagnant and bitter so that he can no longer carry on satisfactorily the task which he took upon himself. To change the metaphor, man has made of Religion *his religion* by cutting it off from its origin and treating it as a tool which he can wholly control. But separated from the source by which it should be constantly repaired and renewed, it has hardened into an obsolete and entirely useless instrument.

Man is therefore no longer able to understand himself, or ever-changing society, or the situation of society and men in the world. He cannot act decisively and effectively. From the disturbance in religion grows the other disturbance of the relation of the individual to society. With this Niebuhr deals in the next work which we consider.

B. Religion and Society: A Question Directed to Society

The young Detroit pastor had directed his first question on the relation of religion and society to himself and the other representatives of religion. When he became Professor of Ethics or, as it is significantly called in America, Applied Christianity, at Union Theological Seminary in New York City, he directed the same question to society. He called his new book *Moral Man and Immoral Society*, and he makes clear in the introduction that the title is to be understood seriously and not as irony.[36]

"Individual men may be moral in the sense that they are able to consider interests other than their own in determining problems of conduct, and are capable, on occasion, of prefering the advantages of others to their own. They are endowed by nature with a measure of sympathy and consideration for their kind, the breadth of which may be extended by an astute social pedagogy. Their rational faculty prompts them to a sense of justice which educational discipline may refine and purge of egoistic elements until they are able to view a social situation, in which their own interests are involved, with a fair measure of objectivity. But all these achievements are more difficult, if not impossible, for human societies and social groups. In every human group there is less reason to guide and check impulse, less capacity for self-transcendence, less ability to comprehend the needs of others and therefore more unrestrained egoism than the individuals, who compose the group, reveal in their personal relationships.

"The inferiority of the morality of groups to that of individuals is due in part to the difficulty of establishing a rational social force which is powerful enough to cope with the natural impulses by which society achieves its cohesion; but in part it is merely the revelation of a collective egoism, compounded of the egoistic impulses of the individuals, which achieve a more vivid expression and a more cumulative effect when they are united in a common impulse than when they express themselves separately and discretely." [37]

Here Niebuhr is attempting to break through the exclusive interest in individuals which is characteristic of traditional theology and to eradicate the mistaken presupposition that the social group is merely the sum of the individuals. As a preacher and theologian, he has done a service which should have far-reaching effects on theological thinking. In ordinary usage, society means the sum total of all good men—the aggregate of bad men is "the masses"—and no attempt is made to investigate the relation of the individual to society or of society to the individual, nor to keep distinct the fundamental difference between individual and society.

The former pastor is especially fitted for such a task because in Detroit this relation was for him the burning question. As he had formerly investigated the line of conflict in the relation between religion and man, so he now turns to man to consider the relation between man and society, to survey from that angle the combat zone of man and society. This is clearly the logical continuation of his earlier work; for if religion is fruitful and active in the life of the individual, the effect should show itself especially in his relation to the group, to society.

Niebuhr's introductory statement of the problem shows how great is the need for this second investigation. The morality of the group is not merely different from the morality of the individual, it is on a much lower level. When the ethics of the individual drops, in the ethics of society the depth of the fall is squared. Society has the unfortunate peculiarity of freeing and even strongly increasing the immoral, anti-social drives of men so that they easily become a guided missile barrage.

Now, since society is one, if not the basic, constituent of human life, this situation must be seriously considered even though the moralists of our time are greatly pained at the thought of it.

"What is lacking among all these moralists, whether religious or rational, is an understanding of the brutal character of all human collectives, and the power of self-interest and collective egoism in all inter-group relations. Failure to recognise the stubborn resistance of group egoism to all moral and inclusive social objectives inevitably involves them in unrealistic and confused political thought. They regard social conflict either as an impossible method of achieving morally approved ends or as a momentary expedient which a more perfect education or a purer religion will make unnecessary. They do not see that the limitations of the human imagination, the easy subservience of reason to prejudice and passion, and the consequent persistence of irrational egoism, particularly in group behavior, make social conflict an inevitability in human history, probably to its very end." [38]

This is strange in itself, but still more peculiar is the fact that "though human society has roots which lie deeper in history than the beginning of human life, men have made comparatively but little progress in solving the problem of their aggregate existence. Each century originates a new complexity and each generation faces a new vexation in it. For all the centuries of experience, men have not yet learned how to live together without compounding their vices and covering each other 'with mud and with blood.' The society in which each man lives is at once the basis for, and the nemesis of, that fulness of life which each man seeks. However much human ingenuity may increase the treasures which nature provides for the satisfaction of human needs, they can never be sufficient to satisfy all human wants; for man, unlike other creatures, is gifted and cursed with an imagination which extends his appetites beyond the requirements of subsistence. Human society will never escape the problem of the equitable distribution of the physical and cultural goods which provide for the preservation and fulfillment of human life." [39]

Thus Niebuhr shows at the very beginning how closely the individual is bound to the group, so that it is "at once the basis for, and the nemesis of, that fulness of life which each man seeks." As man cannot deny that he was born from the most intimate form of human communion and within human society, so he cannot accept any cowardly flight from the world to a hermit's cell as a solution of his problem. The fulfillment of his life lies in the society which is also at the same time his judge, pronouncing sentence upon him.

On the other hand, the unsatisfactoriness of group morality is rooted in the nature of the individual. Society is threatened by its members; its very continuance becomes problematic, because man in distinction from all other creatures can desire and will struggle greedily to possess more than the necessities of life. That we must live together is certain. The only question is how.

"All social co-operation on a larger scale than the most intimate social group requires a measure of coercion. While no state can maintain its unity purely by coercion neither can it preserve itself without coercion." [40]

But this fact also derives from the individual and his relationships.

"The limitations of the human mind and imagination, the inability of human beings to transcend their own interests sufficiently to envisage the interests of their fellowmen as clearly as they do their own makes force an inevitable part of the process of social cohesion." [41]

So Niebuhr immediately puts his finger on the essential factor which makes it possible for men to live and work together—coercion. Regulation by coercion is a necessity because man's limitations are such that he is incapable of curbing himself sufficiently to assure to others space to be themselves. But coercion is possible only through force. Force in itself is neither good nor evil; it can produce both peace and injustice. But it must be bridled and guided if it is to produce the former and prevent the latter. Here lies the closed circle which circumscribes human existence. Man's incapacity requires coercion and coercion demands force. But force itself is always in dire need of the competent direction and control of men.

There is no gain in trying to distract attention from man's own incapacity by calling either force or coercion evil in itself and the source of all evil. Force and coercion are in themselves neutral, and as tools they are not only useful but very necessary. However, man's latent desire to dominate others rather than to restrain himself for their benefit removes almost every check on the use of the tool, and force becomes the chosen instrument in man's antisocial effort to over-ride his fellowmen and exceed his proper limit.[42]

The possibilities of force, we said, are almost unlimited. But its essential limits are inherent in itself and become effective and visible whenever they are exceeded.

"All through history one may observe the tendency of power to destroy its very *raison d'être*. It is suffered because it achieves internal unity and creates external defenses for the nation. But it grows to such proportions that it destroys the social peace of the state by the animosities which its exactions arouse, and it enervates the sentiment of patriotism by robbing the common man of the basic privileges which might bind him to his nation." [43]

Thus force by the law of its own nature repeatedly meets in the course of history a bar to its extension. But this certainty is small comfort, for we also know that when force is hurled back by its inherent boundaries, it at once reverses its destructive power so that centripetal waves of force follow immediately upon the end of the outward drive. We can hardly wait confidently for this reversal as a possible deliverance.

The solution must come from elsewhere, and here we need to remember what Niebuhr has already taught us. Individual men, standing in the battleline must be the mediating link between the source of religion and society in order that the power of renewal can be brought from that source to society. We therefore must follow Niebuhr as he considers what those powers of the individual man are which can be used for the restoration of society. We shall see what bearing man's activity has upon society and its renewal.

"Human beings are endowed by nature with both selfish and unselfish impulses. The individual is a nucleus of energy which is organically related from the very beginning with other energy, but which maintains, nevertheless, its own discrete existence. Every type of energy in nature seeks to preserve and perpetuate itself and to gain fulfillment within terms of its unique genius. The energy of human life does not differ in this from the whole world of nature. It differs only in the degree of reason which directs the energy. Man is the only creature which is fully self-conscious. His reason endows him with a capacity for self-transcendence. He sees himself in relation to his environment and in relation to other life. Reason enables him, within limits, to direct his energy so that it will flow in harmony, and not in conflict, with other life. Reason is not the sole basis of moral virtue in man. His social impulses are more deeply rooted than his rational life. Reason may extend and stabilise, but it does not create, the capacity to affirm other life than his own." [44]

But "it is fair . . . to assume that growing rationality is a guarantee of man's growing morality." [45]

Niebuhr is obviously not the kind of fanatical anti-rationalist who talks of the "harlot reason." On the contrary, he sees in reason, if not the essence of humanity, certainly the place where man's uniqueness is revealed in the self-consciousness which separates him from all other creatures.

Here Niebuhr comes, in the context of social analysis, to the starting point of the complete anthropology which he will later develop. Man sees himself, perhaps we should say man takes a survey of himself—a power which no other creature possesses. And he sees himself at once in a context.

The reasonable and true goal of this self-transcendence and self-survey is for Niebuhr never self-centredness but relatedness to community. There lie both opportunity and danger. Reason as the seat and tool of this human uniqueness makes possible to a certain degree the relation of man to the group, guides and directs that relation. Reason also sets limits to man's action as related to society. But—and this *but* is important—reason does not "create the capacity to affirm other life than his own"; reason only "extends and stabilizes" such capacity. Nor is reason strong enough to guide the course of the "social impulse" when it turns toward society.

Two questions demand further attention. First, what are the roots of the social impulses if they "are more deeply rooted than man's rational life?" Second, just what is meant by limited guidance of the social impulses, what are its inherent dangers and how do they result?

We turn first to the second inquiry, both because its course is clear, and also because the discussion of it will clarify the answer to the first to which it will inevitably bring us back.

"The possibilities of increasing both the rational and the more uniquely moral resources of individuals are so real that it is not surprising that those who study the possibilities should frequently indulge the hope of solving the problems of society by this method. They easily fail to recognise the limits of morality in human life. The possibility of extending reason does not guarantee that it can be extended far enough to give a majority of individuals a comprehension of the total social situation in which they stand. The ability of reason to check impulse does not inevitably provide a sufficient check to prevent the conflict of impulses, particularly the conflict of collective impulses in society. . . .

"Reason may not only justify egoism prematurely but actually give it a force which it does not possess in non-rational nature. Human self-consciousness is the fruit of reason. Men become conscious of themselves as they see themselves in relation to other life and to their environment. This self-consciousness increases the urge to preserve and to extend life. In the animal the instincts of self-preservation do not extend beyond the necessities provided by nature. The animal kills when it is hungry and fights or runs when it is in danger. In man the impulses of self-preservation are transmuted very easily into desires for aggrandisement. There is a pathetic quality in human self-consciousness which accentuates this tendency. Self-consciousness means the recognition of finiteness within infinity. The mind recognises the *ego* as an insignificant point amidst the immensities of the world. In all vital self-consciousness there is a note of protest against this finiteness. It may express itself in religion by the desire to be absorbed in infinitude. On the secular level it expresses itself in man's effort to universalise himself and give his life a significance beyond himself. The root of imperialism is therefore in all self-consciousness.

"Once the effort to gain significance beyond himself has succeeded, man fights for his social eminence and increased significance with the same fervor and with the same sense of justification, with which he fights for his life. The economy of nature has provided that means of defense may be quickly transmuted into means of aggression. There is therefore no possibility of drawing a sharp line between the will-to-live and the will-to-power. Even in the emotions, attitudes of defense and aggression are so compounded, that fear may easily lead to courage, and the necessity of consolidating the triumph won by courage may justify new fears." [46]

We must therefore weigh seriously the limitations of reason, for to ignore them is certainly to incur exactly those dangers which have beset mankind for the last two centuries. Niebuhr demonstrates that reason, just because it makes possible man's self-consciousness and therefore his selfish attitude towards the world around him, also gives him a realization of his nothingness in the universe. And this recognition produces as a compensatory reaction man's capacity to increase his own power at the expense of others in order to win an illusory victory over his own limitations and insignificance, which reason has disclosed to him. This means that reason releases the naturally limited impulses from the context of nature and sets them free for wider uses. The natural will-to-live is transformed into the will-to-power which transcends natural limits. And this transformation occurs so gradually that "there is no possibility of drawing a sharp line between the will-to-live and the will-to-power." Accordingly social and political, even international difficulties are brought into a very close relationship to human self-consciousness. "The root of imperialism is therefore in all self-consciousness."

The consideration of society inevitably leads us back to the individual man, since the centre of the battleline of man and society has been shifted from outside man to man himself. And consequently the contrast implied in the title *Moral Man and Immoral Society* requires qualification. When we look closely, the centre of society's problem lies in man's self-valuation, necessarily a negative valuation, which is the consequence of his self-consciousness with its possibility of self-transcendence. Social disturbances always depend on the recognition of a disturbed relation to the universe. And beyond the visible universe is always the sense of Him who created and preserves it.

We must always keep in mind that the two relationships of man are closely bound together and can never be dissevered. In the spontaneous dependence of man on God as his creator, the harmonious relation of man to his physical environment and to society is included; for God created man not only to rule the rest of creation. He created him also for companionship with it, and this companionship culminates in community with his fellowmen. God created man in His own image, that is in a living communion with God, as a living being responsive to God. The meaning of this image is the clearer, because when God created man for communion with Himself, He also set him in close relation to his fellow creature: "male and female created He them" (Gen. 1:27). The human bond, however, is not separable from nor on a level with man's relation to God on which it depends.

We can now return to the question which we left unanswered: "If man's social impulses are not rooted in reason, what is their origin?" The answer is now clear. Man's social impulses proceed from man's relatedness with his fellowmen as decreed by man's Creator. This answer will be more fully discussed later; it is sufficient here to recognize and state it.

The threat to man's acceptance of his two-fold relationship to God and to the world as normal and unquestioned and hence the threat to the relationship itself came, the story of the Fall tells us, when man became conscious that he was cut off from his Creator in a universe, cold, alien and infinitely wide, so that he himself was menaced with losing himself in nothingness. We are again faced with that which the Bible at the very beginning (Gen. 3) calls sin. In our contemporary situation we meet it as man's subversion of his relation to the world and to society, both of which suffer from disasters engendered by man himself. In man therefore the two combat zones of human relatedness to God and to society unite, although we may call the one sin in the theological sense, and say that the other reveals the moral imperfection of man. A complete separation, as has been said, is never possible, for here we have cause and its effect.

The significance of all this for Niebuhr's thinking is clear. He started with the intention of investigating the centres of conflict in the complex, God-religion-man-society, in order to clarify the right relation of gospel and world. He discovered that the battle-lines of religion-man and man-society not only are conjoined, but also stand in a relation of dependence, the one upon the other. They cannot be compared as equals; the relation to God has absolute precedence over the relation to other men. It is clear that if the cause of disruption originates at one source the restoration must come from the same source. We are then faced with the question, what powers can flow to men from the source of religion which may restore the disruptions in man's relation to society, disruptions for which man is himself to blame?

We have called the disruption man's fault because the actions of men produced it. We have called it moral imperfection because it shows that man fails to act rightly toward society because of his moral shortcomings. We could equally well call it the social-moral result of sin; or use the concept which Niebuhr applies here, *selfishness*. That term describes concretely the nature and the consummation of the disruption. When the fact of selfishness is fully acknowledged, remedies can be compounded.

"If the recognition of selfishness is prerequisite to the mitigation of its force and the diminution of its anti-social consequences in society, religion should be a dominant influence in the socialisation of man; for religion is fruitful of the spirit of contrition. Feeling himself under the scrutiny of an omniscient eye, and setting his puny will into juxtaposition with a holy omnipotent will, the religious man is filled with a sense of shame for the impertinence of his self-centred life. The sentiment of contrition runs as a persistent motif of humility through all classical religious literature and expresses itself in all religious life. It may become so stereotyped and formalised that its inner vitality is lost, but even then it pays tribute to an inner necessity of the religious life." [47]

Niebuhr believes the primary contribution of religion to the "socialisation of man" to be that man sees himself differently because he sees himself in a new context. He is no more forsaken and alone. He is no longer a self-seeking, independent fragment of nothingness facing a wide, impersonal, cold universe. God has lovingly set him in living, inner relatedness to Himself, as ruler of the whole of the rest of creation in order that loving communion may be extended farther into society and the world. Man no longer needs to be self-centred, relating all around him to himself alone and so misusing all; for man is not merely sought by God, he is already found by Him and established in true relatedness to Him so that now through him and from him true relationships penetrate into society.

But the deepest and strongest effect upon man wrought by the new relationship is that he is led by the presence of the omnipotent and omniscient God from forbidden self-direction to the contrite recognition of his real nature and so becomes fit for his proper service in the relatedness of God and society. So society is restored at its innermost core. So society becomes community. Man sees himself, but he sees himself as he is seen by God, therefore in his true nature and position.

Yet mere knowledge of the state of man, however true it be, is not in itself sufficient. The living God who judges our selfishness and transmutes it into humble repentance before Him is the God who wills to communicate His restoring love to society. We ourselves therefore must devote ourselves to society with new insight. Because of our relatedness to God, we are become more sensitive to the wrongs of society. To the righting of those wrongs, the power of God and our service to His power—or rather, God's power working through us—must be directed.

Since it has been demonstrated that the origin of the conflict within society is in men whose bond with God has been broken, we can now examine the consequences and see where the lines of battle lie. Here the correctness of our interpretation will justify itself. When the battlelines which appear so different and so unrelated can be reduced to a single line determined by man's broken relatedness to God, restoration at that line can penetrate all sectors of human society.

It is worth repeating that the especial contribution of Niebuhr lies just here. He has taken man's essential relatedness seriously and has investigated it in all its ramifications. His chief service to contemporary theology is not the systematic expression and exposition of the articles of faith *per se*. But his task as Professor of Applied Christianity he has undertaken with great earnestness, with a surprisingly fresh earnestness; and he has developed this *Applicatio*, the application of Christianity, very fully indeed.

He does not attempt in the fashion of Bacon to conduct the investigation step by step from the centre, the individual man, to the periphery, the widest circles of society where it becomes almost impossible in the welter of national and international assemblies to perceive any human action at all, or any true community of men. He begins boldly at the circumference and hopes by moving toward the centre to reach the individual man. Actually, he is testing his conclusion by analysis. He never assumes that the restoration of society should begin at the periphery. On the contrary, the periphery is where it ends; for it begins at the centre, the individual man joined in true relatedness to God, and proceeds toward the periphery.

"The sharpening of class antagonisms within each modern industrial nation is increasingly destroying national unity and imperilling international comity as well. It may be that the constant growth of economic inequality and social injustice in our industrial civilisation will force the nations into a final conflict, which is bound to end in their destruction. The disintegration of national loyalties through class antagonisms has proceeded so far in the more advanced nations, that they can hardly dare to permit the logic inherent in the present situation to take its course. Conditions in these nations, particularly in Germany where the forces and factors which operate in modern civilisation may be seen in clearest outline, reveal what desperate devices are necessary for the preservation of even a semblance of national unity and how these very devices seem to make for an international conflict in which the last semblance of that unity will be destroyed. If the possibilities and perils of the contemporary situation are to be fully understood it will be necessary to study the class antagonism within the nations carefully and estimate their importance for the future of civilisation." [48]

These words recall what Niebuhr said earlier of force, and we now understand it better since we understand the human motives underlying the use of force. He gives us a true comprehension of national and international struggles for co-existence. Armed international conflict, *war* in its primary sense, is a disturbance of society involving different peoples and turning whole continents into battlefields. But the preparation for war was made by class conflicts whose lines of battle are within one nation. These class conflicts in turn are enlarged and therefore more conspicuous projections of the conflicts of individual men. With painful exactness and at a higher voltage, wars and class conflicts reproduce the individual's misuse of force to save himself from insignificance. What Niebuhr said of the behavior of man to his fellows is equally valid for the relation, or rather for the hostility, between classes. Anyone inclined to question this validity, need only consider the importance which is tacitly and openly accorded to prestige in the struggles of party politics and in world diplomacy.

This problem needs further consideration.

"What is important for our consideration is that inequalities of social privilege develop in every society, and that these inequalities become the basis of class divisions and class solidarity. We have previously seen that inequalities of privilege are due chiefly to disproportions of power, and that the power which creates privilege need not be economic but usually is." [49]

That disproportion of power brings class conflicts is perhaps especially clear today when class differences are due not to differences of birth and lineage but chiefly to economic conditions, so that the attitudes and consequently the points of conflict of the separate classes differ from those of the past.

"The moral attitudes of dominant and privileged groups are characterised by universal self-deception and hypocrisy. The unconscious and conscious identification of their special interests with general interests and universal values, which we have noted in analysing national attitudes, is equally obvious in the attitude of classes. The reason why privileged classes are more hypocritical than underprivileged ones is that special privilege can be defended in terms of the rational ideal of equal justice only by proving that it contributes something to the good of the whole. Since inequalities of privilege are greater than could possibly be defended rationally, the intelligence of privileged groups is usually applied to the task of inventing specious proofs for the theory that universal values spring from, and that general interests are served by, the special privileges which they hold." [50]

A comment of Niebuhr's on this tendency of the privileged classes to obscure facts in order to justify and maintain their privileges throws light on one important aspect of the contemporary scene.

"The human mind is so weak an instrument, and is so easily enslaved and prostituted by human passions, that one is never certain to what degree the fears of the privileged classes, of anarchy and revolution, are honest fears which may be explained in terms of their imperfect perspective upon social facts; and to what degree they are dishonest attempts to put the advancing classes at a disadvantage." [51]

There is another, far-reaching conclusion which is important if we desire to understand and alter the present situation.

"David Hume declared that the maxim that egoism is, though not the exclusive, yet the predominant inclination of human nature, might not be true in fact, but that it was true in politics. He held it to be true in politics since group action is determined by majority opinion and it would always be true that the majority would be actuated by the egoistic motive. It is difficult to read the history of mankind and arrive at any other conclusion. It must be taken for granted therefore that the injustices in society, which arise from class privileges, will not be abolished purely by moral suasion. That is a conviction at which the proletarian class, which suffers most from social injustice, has finally arrived after centuries of disappointed hopes." [52]

It is not a mere misunderstanding on the part of the privileged classes which gives rise to social injustices and perpetuates them. Nor can any attempt to achieve a correct understanding by moral suasion end them. Their underlying cause is the egoistic will-to-power which enslaves and misuses reason. Reason is then employed only to veil the awkward facts and the palpable injustices. Corresponding to this unconscious or conscious dishonesty on the part of the privileged classes is a dishonesty of the unprivileged manifest in an unrealistic hope for the future, combined queerly enough with a sceptical and cynical view of the present.

"If we analyse the attitudes of the politically self-conscious worker in ethical terms, their most striking characteristic is probably the combination of moral cynicism and unqualified equalitarian social idealism which they betray. The industrial worker has little confidence in the morality of men; but this does not deter him from projecting a rigorous ethical ideal for society." [53]

If an indictment of the privileged classes must concern itself with an honest, realistic judgment of the present social situation and the part played in it by human weaknesses and errors; the argument with the proletarians must begin with an honest and realistic survey of the future and of the interests and the conduct of men as they actually are. The hope for the future in the Christian faith and in Marxism have enough resemblance to each other to make necessary a careful investigation of both and an accurate differentiation between them.

"In the eschatology of the true Christian, virtue will ultimately triumph by the power of its own strength, or by the strength supplied by God's grace. In the eschatology of the true Marxian, justice will be established because weakness will be made strong through economic forces operating with inexorable logic in human history. The Marxian imagines that he has a philosophy or even a science of history. What he has is really an apocalyptic vision. A confident prophecy of the future is never more than that. In him political hopes achieve religious proportions by overleaping the bounds of rationally verifiable possibilities, just as, in the soul of the true Christian, moral hopes achieve religious verification. There is something both sublime and ridiculous in expecting either the meek or the weak to inherit the earth, that is, in expecting the disinherited to conquer either by virtue of their moral qualities or by virtue of their very disinheritance. Yet there is an element of truth in both expectations; for there are tendencies in history which make for the casting of the mighty from their seats, both morally and politically." [54]

However, in spite of this, Niebuhr cannot simply acquiesce in the credulous and unsupported hope that the Marxist dream is on the way to fulfillment.

"The expectation of changing human nature by the destruction of economic privilege to such a degree that no one will desire to make selfish use of power, must probably be placed in the category of romantic illusions." [55]

But this means that:
"the question which confronts society is, how can it eliminate social injustice by methods which offer some fair opportunity of abolishing what is evil in our present society, without running the

risk of substituting new abuses and injustices in the place of those abolished. That question raises two issues which the proletarian is not willing to consider. From his perspective there is nothing good in modern society which deserves preservation. In his mood he is not inclined to worry about the future. Like all desperate men he can afford to be romantic about it."[56]

Whatever in the preceding analysis may appear to contradict Niebuhr's former statement that the Marxist is expecting a rosy future must be interpreted in the light of the fact that the proletarian hope of a future Paradise is tied to the impending victorious revolution which will end forever the bourgeois hope of a future to be reached by evolution. A middle class of property holders who are well content with the present and enjoy the deceptive hope of future progress which expresses itself almost in Coué's phrase "every day better and better," is incapable of discerning reality or of estimating those forces which are dynamically preparing for the time ahead.

The attitude of the proletariat is very different. Its members cannot bridge the gap between the present form of society which they absolutely reject and the distant future in which they confidently believe. Accordingly they cannot recognize in the present any good at all which might be worth preserving as an aid to shaping the immediate future. The strictly dialectic assumptions of Marxism are diametrically opposed to the concept of orderly progress, but afford justification for uncritical dreams of the gains to be made in the post-revolutionary epoch. The only possibility which the proletariat sees today is revolution—never evolution.

To summarize briefly the contemporary positions of both the privileged and the unprivileged classes: we find that the privileged have no conception of the necessity of change in the present state of society because they cannot and will not see the actual conditions; while the oppressed exhibit a similar blindness in reverse, seeing no good threads at all in the present social fabric. By them also no improvement is desired—nothing but a swift and complete overthrow. But the basis and motive for holding both positions lie in the nature of men and show themselves in men's attitude toward power. The aim of the privileged is the preservation of his own power; that of the unprivileged is the destruction of an alien power. Both reject the possibility of beneficial basic alteration.

Change therefore must originate in some different and more profound source which can first alter the nature and attitude of men so as to induce in them a new relation to their environment. Again we realize that Niebuhr attacks the problem much more deeply and with much more freedom than either of the two groups. Because he knows that a radical change is necessary—a change in man himself—he is not content with superficial hopes of external change, although he does see possibilities of changes for the better in external circumstances. But if man's own nature remains unchanged, then all external improvements and overturns are useless, for the sun rises the next morning on the same foolish men. Yet if man himself is new-made then both today and tomorrow offer external values which should be preserved as well as situations which must be changed. Neither bourgeoisie nor Marxism have a sense for genuine change. Their efforts are either to preserve or to overthrow.

The *genuine* change of society can be understood and affirmed only by the man who knows that man himself is transformed by the act of God who judges man and by grace creates him anew, so that man can then be the bearer of harmonious change. This conclusion must be demonstrated by a closer look at those groups in social-political life who desire change.

The slogan of the proletariat runs "the Perfect (that is "the classless") Society by Revolution." Now revolution should not be rejected solely because it is cruel. The slow destruction of men by the exploitation and exhaustion of their powers although less obvious and dramatic is, perhaps just because of its gradual and unspectacular character, satanically cruel. Revolution is in itself a natural reaction of despair against the blind obstructionism of the ruling class who reject any moderate alteration in the structure of society. To condemn revolution is foolish so long as we are incapable and unwilling to avert it by removing its causes beforehand and so moderating the compulsion towards it. But revolution as a solution is doomed to fail because it can never actually reach the goal which would justify it, and must consequently remain forever unjustified. Revolution exchanges the holder of power, but it does not change the nature of power-holding.

"The hope that the internal enemies will all be destroyed and that the new society will create only men who will be in perfect accord with the collective will of society, and will not seek personal advantage in the social process, is romantic in its interpretation of the possibilities of human nature and in its mystical glorification of the anticipated automatic mutuality in the communist society." [57]

Even more than that:

"Inequality of reward need not of course, even if it represents a permanent concession to the weaknesses of human nature, as is probably the case, result in the old inequalities of power which breed inequalities of privilege, which are either disproportionate or totally irrelevant to the importance of function and the efficiency with which function is performed. It is possible for society to prevent accumulations of unequal rewards from being transmuted into instruments of social power. But it cannot prevent them from becoming symbols of unequal social prestige. In other words, if the desperate means which the communist uses are to be justified by the totally different and more ideal society which he creates, the justification is not as convincing as it seems to the romantic communist. If the new society does not eliminate the weaknesses of human nature, which cause injustice, as completely as he supposes, he has lost the moral advantage of his absolutism. Perhaps a society which gradually approximates the ideal will not be so very inferior morally to one which makes one desperate grasp after the ideal, only to find that the realities of history and nature dissolve it. Absolutism, in both religious and political idealism, is a splendid incentive to heroic action, but a dangerous guide in immediate and concrete situations. In religion it permits absurdities and in politics cruelties, which fail to achieve justifying consequences because the inertia of human nature remains a nemesis to the absolute ideal." [58]

It is, we see, for wholly realistic reasons that Niebuhr distrusts the Marxist revolutionary idea. It is because revolution shows itself incapable of achieving its goal and leaves unfulfilled the demands which produced it. Niebuhr will later follow out the deeper reasons for the failure; but at this point he turns to the experiences of parliamentary socialism to demonstrate that justice cannot be completely achieved by political power alone.

"Parliamentary socialism is imperilled not only by the loss of the religious absolutism, which characterises unspoiled proletarian thought, but by the temptations which arise from the practical tactics which it must pursue. It must collaborate with other parties in the administration of government. In such co-operation it must try to bargain for the realisation of as much of its programme as the opposition will accept." [59]

"The questions of the personal morality of socialist leaders are of course secondary to the whole problem of maintaining parliamentary socialism as a critical, radical and detached force within a national community and preventing its absorption in the national ethos. We have previously recognised the tremendous power of the sentiment of nationalism and also the practical impossibility of a national community arising to the heights of effective self-criticism. It is probably not too severe a judgment to declare that no group within a nation will ever criticise the nation as severely as the nation ought to be criticised, if it does not stand partly outside of the nation." [60]

From the consideration of these two attempts to better the organization of society, we recognize that the real problem is one of true relatedness and true freedom. It can be expressed "in society but not of society" and the agreement with "in the world . . . not of the world" of the Gospel of John is not accidental.

If the communist can make no useful contribution to the improvement of society, the reason is that by totally rejecting it he has lost his place in it; but the parliamentary socialist is so enmeshed in the complexities of the present that he loses sight of any goal. He can have no effective influence because the needful ability to criticize has been lost, if not through personal ambition and desire for fame, at least through the necessity he feels for co-operation with other parties.

So we meet again the problem of the true relation of man to society and the specific conflicts involved therein. It is clear that we must know not only the location of the battlelines, but also the true position of man in relation to them. In other words, since the conflicts are within society, man if he is rightly to change the wrongs of society must attain a true relatedness to the existing society. But such a true relatedness is possible only if, bound by his obligation as "citizen of another world," he is not completely absorbed into society; if he has won from the sources of religion an untrammeled independence which makes it possible for him to understand the conflicts, to view the struggle as a whole and to speak a word of guidance to society.

It is therefore wholly untrue that man in his double relatedness to God and to society needs only to conserve the two relationships wholly distinct and separate in two entirely discrete and uncombinable areas of life. The relatedness with God through the sources of religion naturally affects man's functioning in society, and his proper function in society, as we have learned, requires him to be related to God in order to be the mediating link between God and society.

These extracts from Reinhold Niebuhr's book have told us much more about his conception of the problem than we should learn by proceeding further into the beginnings of his attempts at solution. These are unclear and are grasped intuitively rather than rationally. They also show that in this early period of Niebuhr's creative thinking he has only begun to realize the extent of the problem or to develop its solution.

Certainly it would be exceedingly interesting to follow out all the attempts at solution, however incomplete, which Niebuhr offers and to see how far from clear and precise both the conception of the problem and the answer remain because the basic problem of human sin had not yet come with its full force into Niebuhr's thought. However such an investigation would entirely exceed the limits of this work. It is also unnecessary because, since we are to follow the further course of his thinking, we can later take a critical look backward and note the contrast between the beginning and his later widened and deepened comprehension. We shall then judge Niebuhr's progress more truly, and perhaps escape the danger of estimating him unfairly and from our own presuppositions.

C. Religion and Society: A Question of their Mutual Evaluation

We have in the foregoing considered the relation of religion and society to each other as two opposite poles. We have learned that the centre of the whole disturbance of their relationship lies in man as the mediator of the relationship. But before we come finally to the discussion of man as the mediator, we should first ask whether the two poles are in themselves capable of being related. We shall seek to discover whether religion is able to found a society which is a true community and whether society is susceptible of being formed by religion into a true community.

The need for this question is clear from the fact that the two social movements discussed in the preceding section agree, although for different reasons, in a negative answer. Parliamentary socialism holds, in agreement with other movements based on evolutionary hypotheses, that a socializing of society by religion is unnecessary because it will occur without the influence of religion through the further secular development of society.

Proletarian communism considers it impossible because the socialization of society cannot be achieved without a totally destructive revolution. For the necessity of total revolution, religion is chiefly responsible because both *ex officio* and *de facto* it acts as a conserving and therefore as an anti-progressive force.

The preceding inquiry is narrowed and pointed in the question, "Are religion and society capable of mutual interaction toward the creation of true community?" Reinhold Niebuhr has undertaken to answer this question in a book with the title, *The Contribution of Religion to Social Work*.[61] He begins by stating the criticism directed against religion.

"The most obvious weakness of religion in social action is that it seems always to create a spirit of generosity within terms of a social system, without developing an idealism vigorous or astute enough to condemn the social system in the name of a higher justice. Religion, in other words, is more fruitful of philanthropy than of social justice. It might be claimed that this tendency reveals not so much a weakness of religion, as a natural limitation of the human imagination. The average man does not have an intelligence keen enough to question the social structure in which he stands. Since it is older than he, he easily lends himself to the illusion that it is eternal and immutable. He has not seen the historical processes which gave it birth, and he has little confidence therefore in the possibility of its transmutation. Since religion, however, always carries with it a sense of the absolute which prompts it to condemn present realities from the perspective of perfection and to dream of a day when perfect love and justice will be attained, there must be some special reason for its frequent easy and uncritical acceptance of the social situation in which it exists." [62]

Niebuhr sees that man with only his own intelligence is not capable of judging objectively his own social situation. Religion gives him precisely this power and consequently imposes this obligation upon him. Man must see and judge the social structure of which he is a part *sub specie aeternitatis*. But religion as a human institution, cut off from the source of religion, is precisely what prevents this function of religion from being fully exercised in social work.

Niebuhr finds the fundamental reason for this failure to be three different weaknesses of religion in its human institutional manifestations.

1. Religious Pessimism

"The absolute perfection, the holiness of God, the ideal of the Kingdom of God, which are religion's standard of comparison with present realities, betray it into a complete pessimism as to the possibility of saving the world. The world of injustice is taken for granted. It was destined to be evil by the fall of man and it will not be saved except as it is saved by divine intervention." [63]

2. Religious Determinism

"Another root of the social conservatism of religion, which tempts it to practice charity within the limitations of a social system without raising ultimate questions about the justice of the system itself, is the natural determinism of religion. To the religious imagination, God is at one moment the ideal towards which all things must strive and by comparison with which all contemporary social standards are convicted of inadequacy; and in the next moment he is the omnipotent creator of all things, whose power and wisdom guarantees that goodness of existing social organizations. . . . Paul put the logic of this determinism clearly in Romans 13:1–2: 'Let every soul be subject unto the higher powers. For there is no power but of God; the powers that be are ordained of God. Whosoever therefore resisteth the power, resisteth the ordinance of God.' . . .

"It must not be assumed, however, that the tendencies toward determinism in the history of Christianity rest upon a single scriptural phrase. The idea that social and political arrangements must be virtuous because they exist under an omnipotent God who could change them if he would, grows out of a natural inclination in the very heart of religion, the inclination to aggrandize the object of worship, God, until it becomes coextensive with the whole of reality." [64]

3. Religious Individualism

"Another reason why a religiously inspired ethical sensitivity is more likely to create philanthropy than social justice, is that religion is constitutionally preoccupied with the motives of ethical actions and finds it difficult to deal with an entire social situation.

Religion is more interested in the development of the spirit of love in the hearts of men as a mark of personal perfection, than in love as an instrument of social redemption. The absurd suggestion that the poor afford the rich an occasion for the exercise of philanthropy is rather closer to the logic of religion than a sympathetic critic would like to admit." [65]

Here we have an explicit analysis of the differences in the human understanding of religion and of the consequent misinterpretations of the nature of religion which prevent man from bringing the forces which come to him from the source of religion to the rescue and service of society. Man rejects religion as a help in seeing injustices and in instituting appropriate changes in the structure of society. The investigation which Niebuhr here proposes is to make clear the limitations of the contributions of institutional religion to social work. In order to do this, we must consider somewhat more closely the positive contribution.

"Religion is first of all a force of order and unity in the lives of individuals. Men differ from brutes, in that the impulses of their lives do not possess a natural and inevitable harmony and unity. There are dozens of different ways in which the forces with which we are endowed by nature may be integrated. The dynamics of life may be directed into many different channels, according as personal inclination and family and national tradition, prompt the choice of a dominant interest or sanction a particular type of behavior. Any one of many varying impulses may become the organizing center of a life, and the other impulses may be grouped around it in many patterns and configurations. The unity and order of a life depend upon the emotional power and the moral inclusiveness of that life's guiding principle. . . . Ideally, religion is the commitment of life to the highest values, conceived as the will of God. The moral potency of Christ in the Christian religion is derived from the fact that he is to the religious imagination the symbol of the best that life can be. The individual who commits himself to Christ usually does not, and may never, fully understand the significance of all the ethical positions which are associated with the historical Jesus. Sometimes the symbol remains devoid of any specific moral meaning. It stands in general only for the good life, the specific meaning of which is given by the problems which the individual faces and the circumstances in which he stands." [66]

Since man as the connecting link in the relation between God and society is both the centre of its disturbance and the place where something new must come into being, what has just been quoted concerning the individual has a meaning which reaches beyond the individual and applies to society as a whole. Society must be integrated within itself if it is not to be broken into fragments in its own conflicts. The nucleus for its crystallization is the individual man, and religion through the medium of the individual man can meet the pressing and essential needs of society. Niebuhr here first of all presents the task of religion in a wholly concrete fashion. Religion in certain men and through them in society assumes the function which Nature performs in the instinctive life of all other creatures. To man, whose self-consciousness and voluntary control of his own existence demand integration on a new and higher plane, religion should offer the centre of this integration; and this centre should bind together and control the whole life of man.

But characteristically Niebuhr finds the real significance of the restoring power of religion not in man's self-integration but in his self-dedication to a goal which transcends himself.

"If traditional religion is able to prevent chaos, a vital religion is able to resolve it. The experience of conversion which rationalized types of religion tend to discredit and which conventionally unified and integrated personalities find irrelevant to their needs, has always been a potent force in bringing order out of confusion for those who, having become victims of their passions, have failed to achieve a decent order and unity in their lives." [67]

We have here reached the centre of our whole question. Man as the connecting link in the relatedness of God and society is at the same time the point where all the possible disturbances and conflicts converge. From the disintegration of the individual all other disturbances radiate as effects and consequences. The problem of the relatedness of God and society is centred in the corruption of human personality and the rupture of man's bond to God and to society. And this rupture, in which we can easily recognize once more what the Bible calls sin, presents us with an inseparable triad. From man's loss of his true relatedness to God proceeds the corruption of man's personal self. The result of this corruption is not only the loss of the man's relation to society; society in turn becomes corrupted even to the final consummation of international ruin—world war.

Niebuhr is certainly right in believing that the progress towards total ruin moves in this direction and not in the opposite direction. With equal certainty he affirms that the restoration of true relatedness must proceed from the spring whose stoppage produced the ruin—the source of religion. From this source flow the powers which enable man to turn away from his corrupting and destructive pursuit of unnatural self-will for which he rejected his God-given and God-willed station, and to turn back toward inner and meaningful communion with God and society. Thus Niebuhr fills with fresh meaning the discarded and maligned concept of repentance.

But lest we should think that this understanding of man and of his position has been won by some kind of confused double vision, first from religion outward and then from society as the other pole of human relationship, Niebuhr leaves us in no doubt that the requisite perspective for true insight into man in his fallen state and the only prospect for his healing can be found at one point only, the view-point of religion.

"In classical religion there is always a paradoxical attitude toward human nature. Man is both a child of God and a sinner. The same God who loves man also convicts him of sin. For in the insight of true religion, God is not only loving but holy. He is not only the companion of man's way, but the goal toward which he is striving. In comparison with His holiness, man falls short and feels himself 'an unprofitable servant.' He regards 'all his righteousness as filthy rags.' There is always the suggestion that man ought to love his brethren not because they are, in the sight of God, as good as he, but because they are no worse. 'All have fallen short of the glory of God.' True religion produces not only love, but humility; and the love is partly a derivative of the spirit of contrition. We must forgive those who have wronged us, because we know the same evil to be in us. If we are not without sin, we cannot cast the contumelius stone." [68]

We shall merely state here what we shall later explain more fully, that Niebuhr expects to derive from religion a true evaluation not only of man, but also of society and of the whole world situation. For it is the loving God who reveals to us our ambiguity, our sinful self-entanglement, and the accompanying false judgment of the world around us. So God created in us the possibility of repentance and humility—the attitude which makes possible a new relatedness to God and society.

In dealing with man and his problem, Niebuhr does not confine himself to individual piety nor even to the salvation of man by faith. He goes directly to the task of considering the connection between religion and social work in modern life, and he consistently presents to us the sequence: God turns to man and through man to society.

Before we follow him further, we must make one statement to which we shall later devote more consideration. We must guard ourselves against the false assumption that Niebuhr finds in society the final meaning and purpose for both the divine act of redemption and for human existence. For Niebuhr it is as true of society as of the individual man that "God is . . . the goal toward which he is striving." In a later discussion of history, Niebuhr expresses this with entire clarity, but the belief is already basic to his thinking, and must be taken into account if we are not to misunderstand him.

Let us now turn to what he has to say about the relation of religion to social work in modern life.

"The most significant characteristic of modern life, from the perspective of the spiritual and social needs of modern men, is the technological nature of our civilization. Modern means of production and communication have created a society in which millions of men are brought into terms of economic interdependence without having any necessary organic relationship or sense of moral and spiritual fellowship. . . . The modern machine has, in short, made neighbors strangers, and strangers neighbors. We do not know those who live near to us, and we are dependent upon those who are far from us.

"Furthermore, the same means of production and communication which have increased the extent and intensity of social cohesion, have centralized economic and social power. All essential power in our modern society is economic power, the power of ownership. Economic power is always able to bend political power to its own uses." [69]

Both economic and political power weaken and destroy personal responsibility. The single, little man is engulfed by them and can no longer see, still less exercise, any personal responsibility for the whole. Community life in a city is dissipated in complete particularism. Here good will can only offer "relief" which does not even satisfy the philanthropic inclination to "do good." There is no general sense of responsibility, nor any idea of possessing power over these two powers. For such an idea, one must think realistically enough to recognize that the power of the exploiter can be broken only if the exploited join together and establish a power of their own strong enough to encounter the other. The social and the religious idealists were never sufficiently realistic to deal radically with the actual circumstances and situations of life.

When we read that the question of society is plainly and exclusively a question of power, we may ask whether religion can have any real place or influence in society. Certainly religion cannot simply adopt an economic program or endorse a political party; yet it must not isolate itself from the representatives of any group which is protesting against specific acts of injustice or against the generally accepted inequity of the present social structure. Religion gives to man, because God has come to him with His grace in spite of his sins, a new awareness; so that the insensitivity of one who strives only to maintain his own rights is permeated by loving understanding of the needs of other men. And even more significant—the man who stands as a repentant and humble sinner, pardoned, before his God will believe no longer that salvation must or can come within the present social order as represented and probably influenced by himself. He stands open and ready for the change of all that now is, a change which will be wrought directly from the source of religion. He will be ready for the breaking and renewing of all human achievements by the silent judgment of God.

Niebuhr therefore can never see only right or only wrong on the two opposing sides in the continuing social conflict. On the contrary, he believes that it is the divisive severance of society into two opposing classes which destroys in each the true understanding of the other and of society itself. He therefore does not fall into the mistake of demanding from religion a mere social program, for no program would remove the basic evil of man's lack of true insight. It is left to religion to give to man from its source a true knowledge of himself and therefore of his true place in society.

"True religion prompts to both love and humility, and the humility preserves the unselfish man from assuming that he is unselfish. If he is truly religious, both the insights of the past and a knowledge of himself will help him to realize how much of selfishness is always compounded with unselfishness in the generous deed. The truly religious man does know himself as no one else does. He is an adept at profound introspection, and the criteria with which he approaches the task of introspection are those which have the touch of perfection upon them. He feels himself falling short of the holiness of God. Unfortunately, religion can be used more easily to encourage moral conceit, than to produce humility. For it is only religion at first-hand that prompts to humility. Second-hand religion easily sanctifies conventional virtues as final revelations of the will of God. Wherever the church achieves a really vital religion, it is able to mitigate the animosities of the social struggle by robbing the privileged classes of the moral conceit which is one of their chief weapons, as well as a principal cause of their political intransigeance." [70]

The starting point for the re-creation of the integrity of society lies therefore indubitably in man. Man's view of man, his knowledge of himself as being and acting, must be reconstituted in order that he may gain a new view of society and be able to contribute to the renewing of the social order. But as the individual, if he is too much involved in the power struggles of society, is incapable of disinterested service to society—the experience of parliamentary socialism illustrates this—so also religion itself cannot fulfil its due service to man and bring him to a true and objective knowledge of himself when it has become as Niebuhr phrases it "second-hand," when it has become in a bad sense "churchified" and institutionalized, fit for man's use in the furthering of his own aspirations. Then religion, separated from its origin, has hardened into a traditional mold, shaped by its custodians to secure their own advantage and passed like any other object from one hand to another.

So the investigation comes back again to the beginning of our inquiry, to a question for religion. But to Niebuhr it is equally important to prevent the question addressed to religion from becoming a private tête-a-tête between religion and the individual man. He is greatly concerned to show the whole line of God's controlling power over religion, the line which must be drawn to men and then continued to society. Here, in the discussion of the relation between the individual and society appears for the first time the characteristic conception which is later to become one of the foundation pillars of Niebuhr's concept of society and history.

"The religious ideal, the absolute conceived as the goal of history, is not only a personal ideal, but a social one. Religion has always dreamt of the Kingdom of God. It has always believed in some kind of millennium. Only the extreme individualism of middle-class religion, in the past two centuries, has narrowed the religious vision to the individual life, and made personal immortality and perfection the sole goal of religious striving. In the religion of the prophets and in the gospel of Jesus, there is a vision of a redeemed society. It is very probable that the political means necessary for the achievement of a just society have never been clearly envisaged by any religion. It was always expected that the social redemption would come by divine intervention, though it must be noted that not infrequently the intervention was conceived of in political terms. God was to use the wrath of man to praise him, and to make

Assyrians and Egyptians the tools of his purposes. Religion has, of course, always had a moral ideal which proceeded from a sensitive individual conscience, rather than from the life of the group. It meant that ideal to be applicable for the group, however. Jesus' ideal of love is probably too high for the attainment of any nation. No nation, or any other group for that matter, will ever sacrifice itself for another. The perfect ideal for the individual is too high for intergroup relations. Groups will do well to approximate justice, rather than love. But the perfection of the religious goal can be instrumental in prompting the religious man to assume a highly critical attitude toward all contemporary social arrangements: they fall short of the kingdom of God." [71]

Three of Niebuhr's assertions will be found to be of especial importance for our understanding of the structure of his thought.

1. In the constant dynamic alteration of the forms of society, alteration which should neither be repudiated nor avoided, religion provides the real motive force. Therefore religion unquestionably stands on the side of the impending, of the new. If Niebuhr is convinced that in our day the future in an industrial civilization belongs unconditionally to the proletariat, then he is also sure that the force of vital religion is on the side of the proletariat.

But it is essential for the understanding of the first statement to hold firmly to the second.

2. The truth, "the ultimate truth is with neither type of religion, because men happen to be both individuals and members of social groups." [72] Both are equally important. No type of religion can or ought to boast that it possesses religion or *the* religion. Man stands, indeed, before God, through his religion singled out by God's loving demand upon him, and responding as an individual with love to God. Yet the same God does not allow man to be solitary in his religion, but wills to send him to his brothers so that a true society may arise through a loving association founded on the love of God.

3. Hence it follows that the criterion of religion understood as our human attempt to answer the call of the loving God, must

be how man's ineradicable individuality functions in the service of society. When it fails to function in society, then individual religion founders in its social task. On the other hand, proletarian religion refuses to recognize the depths of life which God reveals only in the loving relationship of "I and Thou."

All three assertions are included in one statement which today, as in all times of uncertainty and insecurity, is greatly needed. "Only religion has the power to destroy the old and build the new." [73]

Niebuhr sees two movements meeting today at one point. On the one hand, by the industrialization of the structure of society, the middle-class culture which bore the stamp of the individual is transformed into an era of proletarianism. But none the less religion, if it is to fulfil its task and preserve its essential character, must accomplish its definitive service to society through the individual in order that the individual again may be accorded his rightful place in his relation with society. The point of intersection of the two movements lies in the problem of man and society. Niebuhr's statement of the problem runs somewhat as follows. In order that the change of society in our time may develop organically, the bourgeois man must learn to see himself and accept himself as a responsible member of society and must also recognize that he is restricted by society. And he must also accept both the inherent dangers and all the positive possibilities of community living—accept them explicitly, assentingly and even creatively. The proletariat on their side must accept the nature of the individual man with all its depths and recognize his fruitful possibilities. Otherwise the proletariat will fail to reach their goal because of their false assumptions regarding the essential factor, man. If they do not see man as he is, they will find themselves after all their struggles cheated of the prize. For the man who formerly perpetrated injustice will still be the same kind of man and his actions will invalidate the justification of the revolutionary overthrow and the sacrifices made for it.

Religion then is prevented by the dynamic energies of its

source from absolutizing itself in its institutional character. It becomes the motivating force which truly binds man to God and allows human personality to function under obligation to society, yet supported by God in freedom. Because God loves man as a person, the individual man must not be lost in the proletarian mass. Because the love of God compels man to brotherhood with his fellowmen, individual irresponsibility in society becomes impossible. True community is created. When the will of God is fulfilled in a community of persons, there is also the fulfillment of the individual self.

But during the development of a social shift the true relation between religion, individual and society is underlined as the fundamental problem of life for all three in their similar difficulties. This Niebuhr has in mind when he so sharply and stubbornly depicts the many displacements in this inclusive arch in order that they may lead us by their own consequences to the one central disturbance of human existence, to the sin of man.

D. Religion and Society: A Question from All Ages to Our Age

It may be partly because the inheritance of a family of famous German historians is alive in Reinhold Niebuhr that he wanders less than other thinkers into the timelessness of abstract speculation. He makes an especial effort to understand the temporal, the passing of time and the distinguishing character of our own time. He seeks with unusual sensitivity to recognize and to point out "the signs of the time." We are reminded of the words already quoted:

"However, since I am not so much scholar as preacher, I must confess that the gradual unfolding of my theological ideas has come not so much through study as through the pressure of world events. Whatever measure of Christian faith I hold today is due to the gradual exclusion of alternative beliefs through world history." [74]

These are not the words of a theologian seeking a purely theoretical interpretation of the present time. Professor Niebuhr feels his responsibility to demonstrate to the age in which he lives that the faith which he is called to preach gives ample help to his contemporaries, dismayed by the events which confront them. Like every true Christian minister, Niebuhr knows that for the preacher, the "Hic est Rhodus, hic salta" means that here and now he must proclaim the gospel as a potent and effectual force. Faith manifests itself in time and for the time, or it is not true faith. So for Niebuhr, time (which in the Bible has a significance wholly different from that given to it in extra-Biblical thought) has an especial meaning. He feels himself primarily the instrument of the timely and time-fulfilling demand of God upon men as that demand is made known through the word of the Bible.

Further, Niebuhr's honesty and his deep confidence in the power and reality of the Christian message allow him to consider seriously and without perturbation other systems of belief until they be progressively excluded by the course of history. If we are to follow the development of Niebuhr's thinking, a double path lies ahead at this point. On the one hand, the uniqueness and the decisive significance of the Christian faith becomes ever clearer in the sequence of world events. On the other hand, conversely, other systems of belief will by the same judgment be progressively excluded.

Before proceeding further with Niebuhr's exposition of the meaning of time, we shall consider a work which surveys the course of history up to the present, treating especially its historical and spiritual significance and dealing specifically with that view of time which Niebuhr was discarding. It is entitled *Reflections on the End of an Era.*

The essential character of this era which is nearing its end—

Niebuhr calls it sometimes capitalistic, sometimes liberal, and often with a shade of contempt "bourgeois civilization"—is, as he sees it, its failure to recognize the true nature of man and consequently of society. The power of reason has been over-valued and that of impulse under-valued. The view of man was unfair and untrue. Change, therefore, must and will come not in outward circumstances, but in man's understanding of himself.

"No stable equilibrium is ever reached in history between the two impulses: the impulse to subject the individual or social ego to the universal even to the point of self-annihilation or absorption and the impulse to universalize the ego even to the point of destroying or enslaving all competing forms of life." [75]

The point of departure was wrong:

"a capitalistic period of society was ushered in by a philosophy of liberalism, the economics of *laissez-faire* and the ethics of utilitarianism. The common note in all these viewpoints was that life was to be made secure and the social structure was to be made permanent by a rational and prudent adjustment of life to life. According to the theory of Adam Smith, the self-interest of competing individuals would automatically make for social harmony. According to the utilitarians, social harmony would be achieved if the force of self-interest were to be qualified by a prudence which knew how to include the general interest in the self-interest." [76]

There are two serious results from this false view.

1. "The whole tragic conflict between the ethical and the imperial force in life is effaced in a theory which does superficial justice to both ["the heights to which life may rise" and "the depths to which it may sink"]. That is how the liberal culture of modernity is defective in both religious profundity and political sagacity. An adequate religion develops only where the ethical impulse is set in vivid juxtaposition to the forces of nature in man; and man is forced both to seek after an impossible victory and to adjust himself to an inevitable defeat. An adequate politics is possible only if the task of achieving some kind of decent harmony in social relations is essayed with a clear understanding of the stubborn inertia which every social purpose meets in the egoism of individuals and groups." [77]

This means that because of the superficiality and incorrectness of the view of man, the forces which could have brought remedy did not come into action. The influx of force is proportional to the tension which provokes the influx.

2. "The moral superficiality of modern culture betrayed it into an easy faith that reason had conquered or could conquer and restrain the anarchic impulses which express themselves in man-as-nature. It had not realized that reason may be used much more easily to justify impulse and to invent instruments for its efficacious expression than to check and restrain impulse. That was a fatal mistake because it permitted a more unrestrained expression of impulse than ever before in history." [78]

It is highly significant that Niebuhr finds the origin of evil and the seed of the decline of the capitalistic era of society in a false view of man. This opinion he never abandons. Not only can he trace to the wrong view of man all the failures and disasters of that form of society which is still apparently dominant. What is still more important, he is led to the conclusion that a new era of humanity can be victoriously attained only with a new and definitive view of humanity. The effort to attain such a view, or at the least to help towards its attainment appears in all the years of creative work which follow. We have here come to the inner turning point of his development, as he himself once expressly affirmed.[79]

A theoretical concept of man may precede by a longer or shorter interval, the effects of the concept on history; but that its effects are actual and momentous cannot be denied. In liberal epochs (liberal in a double sense, philosophical-theological and economic), the harnessing of the beneficent forces is balanced on the other side by a freeing of impulses with anti-social and destructive aims. Such impulses, since there is no guard against them, unfold autonomously and without hindrance. Their activity is directed by the nature of the situation against society which seeks to subject all forces to itself, and the rebellious opposition finally produces what society sought chiefly to prevent—the acceleration of its own destruction.

"Man's higher degree of self-consciousness and egocentricity transmutes the brute's will-to-survive into the human will-to-power." [80]

"Therefore every social system, faced by the peril of death, is bound to make one final and ruthless effort to avert its doom by destroying or suppressing competing forms of life." [81]

"Thus a dying social order hastens its death in the frantic effort to avoid or postpone it." [82]

"There is a profound truth in the religious insight which ascribes death to sin: 'The wages of sin is death.' The judgment is not wholly true; for senility as well as sin causes death. Every organism in nature has its apportioned day and sinks into dust when its day is done. That applies to social organisms as much as to biological ones. Yet in the specific instance death is infrequently due to senility alone. Senility is only a contributory cause. What is most robust, in social history as well as in field and forest, lives at the expense of other life and dies when it can no longer protect itself against the enmity which its predatory life has prompted. Since death in history and in nature comes by senility as well as by sin all purely moralistic interpretations of history are mistaken. A social system simply outlives its usefulness; and its temper and tempo, its presuppositions and organizations fail to meet the requirements of a new situation. It must therefore give way to a new social system which is better fitted to organize life under new conditions. Yet all life, in both nature and history, is driven by immediate impulses to an egoism which is incompatible with the ultimate requirements of survival. It therefore perishes because of its 'sin'. Thus every social system develops disproportions of power and privilege, greater than any rule of justice would sanction, and dangerous to its own longevity." [83]

Here we gain a significant understanding of what constitutes for Niebuhr the nature of sin. We find it, also significantly, in a double connection. Sin is closely interwoven with the nature and life of men. Therefore it can never be separated from man's being as mere action and corrected by maxims of morality. It exists in close conjunction with life itself and with life's limited and temporal character.

Further, for Niebuhr sin is never something which takes place merely between God and man; it has also its different manifestations and consequences in man's relations with the world around him. We shall later consider how these two aspects of sin and their significance for society more and more engage Niebuhr's thinking.

Since Niebuhr is persuaded that for both history and society the determinative foundation does not lie in the rational and lucid realm of reason, he believes that both the interpretation of history and conclusions about history must leave room for the reality of the non-rational which liberal culture could neither measure nor even admit as existing. Certainly thinking cannot of itself impose categories upon the non-rational. But it ought not to turn this inability into the error of limiting itself to itself and excluding the non-rational from reality. Just because of this inability, it must strive to leave space in the realm of reason where the non-rational may stand independently according to its own prescriptions, even though its presence may (as it certainly will) lead to serious tensions and possibilities of error.

There can obviously never be a form or content which is adequate to the affirmation of the non-rational. This difficulty Niebuhr seeks to resolve by the concept of *myth*. Myth provides him with a key to the understanding of history and society at precisely the point where pure rationality loses its pertinence, and, if it still persists, becomes absurd. Myth as the self-expression of the non-rational within rationality appears, Niebuhr believes, at the beginning of the life of society, accordingly at the beginning of history; it accompanies the course of history, and always re-appears where history is confronted by an aim which transcends it, in order to express again in particular terms the end and goal of history. Myth as supra-historical and supra-rational speech in the realms of history and rationality is especially the language of the Bible to reveal from beyond the boundary of society and history the nature of both in their relation to God. Therefore mythological expression appears in its most consummate form where it treats of the beginning of history as established by God, of the beginning of society in the creation of man by God, and of the destruction, by man in the "Fall," of this first unquestioned relatedness of God and man. It comes again to full expression when the theme is the end of society in time, the termination of history in its fulfillment in and by God, and equally in the theme of God's judgment upon the destruction by man of the inter-relatedness of God, man and society.

As certainly as society and history are comprehensible to man only so far as they are seen as what happens to and through man, so surely can they be understood in their depth and their transcendent design and goal only if mythological expression is admitted. For myth shows the true origin of man and his situation as coming from God and sets everything which may occur in the right perspective. Myth and history, even though incompatible, belong together and are inseparable. History is and remains incomprehensible unless it can be brought into sharp relief and evaluated by its possible fulfillment and fulfilled possibility in and through the transcendent God. So only can the disturbance that is sin, with the resultant abyss and the hopelessness of men, be recognized as the prime ingredient of human inadequacy and confusion. And so only is revealed the new possibility of relatedness to God—a possibility created by the overcoming by the Son of God in history of that damage which man has wrought in the relatedness between God and man.

The Cross as the centre between creation and final judgment is the place at which from either side the purely mythological, supra-historical language of the Bible is immediately related to historical event—so clearly and intimately related that without mythological expression the historical event can no more be understood than can its factual historical results. At the Cross where the stark reality and the whole meaning of human confusion and ruin are for the first time dazzlingly illuminated, at this central point of conflict, all things are understood in the light radiating from the one event. Here myth in Niebuhr's sense and history are so closely bound together that although by nature they cannot coincide, they remain wholly inseparable.

Within the limits of the present investigation, we cannot include all the considerations and consequences which follow from

Niebuhr's understanding of myth. (They may be dealt with in a later work.) Here we can only show briefly the direction in which such a discussion would proceed. We can best begin by stating briefly what Rudolf Bultmann has said of his understanding of myth as it is developed in his treatise *Neues Testament und Mythologie.*[84] We shall see that Bultmann and Niebuhr understand the concept *myth* very differently, although the difference cannot be illustrated merely by a series of selected quotations.

We shall first state briefly Bultmann's understanding of myth and show how it contrasts with Niebuhr's and then let Niebuhr himself explain his concept of myth in his own words.

1. We begin with a statement of Bultmann's which apparently could include Niebuhr's conception.

"In myth there finds expression the faith that the known and manageable world in which man lives does not have its source nor its goal in itself, that its foundation and its boundaries lie beyond the known and the manageable, that this known and manageable is permeated, directed and threatened by the uncanny powers which form its basis and its limits. At the same time, myth expresses the knowledge that man is not master of himself, but is essentially dependent upon that which is beyond the known forces governing the world, and that in this very dependence he becomes free from the dominance of the known powers."[85]

But as the next quotations will show, the primary cause and the purpose of mythological language are understood very differently by Bultmann and by Niebuhr.

2. Niebuhr affirms that myth expresses a supra-rational and supra-historical truth about men. With this Bultmann disagrees at three points. Myth does not express a truth in the sense of objective validity, but is an expression of subjective understanding of the self. Myth is not supra- but sub-rational. Finally myth is not supra-historical but is on the contrary an immanent expression of history, so limited by time and bound to time that it must of necessity be transcended.

"The true import of myth is not to give a picture of the objective world. It expresses rather the way in which a man understands *himself* in his world. Myth should not be interpreted cosmologically but anthropologically—or better existentially. Myth speaks of the power or powers which man believes he experiences as the foundation and the limits of his world and of his own action and emotion. He really speaks of those powers in a way which can bring them into conceivable relations with the circle of the known world and its objects and forces, and with the circle of human life with its emotions, aims and possibilities. So he talks of a world-egg or a world-tree in order to make the origin and the foundation of the world conceivable; or he talks of the wars of the Gods out of which arose the circumstances and the laws of the known world. Of what is not world, he speaks in terms of the world; in human terms, he speaks of the Gods." [86]

"Therefore in the myth itself is included the necessity of criticising it; that is, its objective presentation must be treated critically, since the true purpose of myth—to speak of a power 'beyond' to which world and man are subject—is impeded and obscured by the objectifying character of the expression. Even in the mythology of the New Testament, the essential truth is not to be sought in the objective content, but in the understanding of existence expressed by the objective representations. The important question is the truth or falsity of this understanding of existence. Faith affirms that truth; but faith must not be required to accept the mythological picture of the world presented in the New Testament." [87]

"The picture of the world in the New Testament is mythological." [88]

"The representation of the history of redemption, which is the content of the New Testament, corresponds to a mythical picture of the world. The gospel is proclaimed in the language of mythology." [89]

"All this is mythological language and the various motifs can easily be traced back to the contemporary myths of Jewish apocalyptic and the gnostic myth of salvation. So far as it is mythological language, it is unbelievable to the man of today, because for him that mythological picture of the world has vanished. Contemporary proclamation of the Christian message is faced with the question whether when it demands faith from men it expects them to accept this vanished mythical picture of the world. If such acceptance is impossible, the question arises whether the message of the New Testament presents a truth which is independent of the mythical world picture. If so, then the task of theology would be to de-mythologize the Christian message.

"Can the Christian message expect men today to accept the mythological picture of the world as true? Such an expectation is foolish and impossible. Foolish—for the picture is not as such specifically Christian; it is simply the world picture of a vanished age, and certainly was not the result of scientific thinking. Impossible—because a man cannot adopt a picture of the world by an act of will. He already has a picture given to him as a part of his historical environment." [90]

Here the difference between Bultmann and Niebuhr becomes clearer. For Niebuhr, myth is the word of God to man, coming to him from beyond the boundaries of human knowledge; it is the word which sets man right, which re-integrates him. Its form and content belong together, essentially and inseparably; for man himself is ignorant of the actuality of the relation between God and man, and therefore ignorant also of the truth of his own existence in relatedness to God and to his fellowmen. For Niebuhr, therefore, myth is the word of God, spoken in our language in order that man may learn from God that truth which is not an objective thing but the living and reciprocal relatedness of God and men.

Myth does not originate from man, and therefore it cannot and must not be eliminated by man. On the contrary, when man feels himself drawn by God into this living relatedness—which always affects society within time as a whole—his actual experience leads him to affirm that myth expresses THE truth of his existence, truth which he by himself and by reason alone, could never have realized nor expressed. Therefore myth becomes meaningful for him as the revealing word of God; he has experienced its fulfillment. It could perhaps be expressed: myth becomes for man at once essential and existential.[91]

Bultmann's judgment is very different. For him, myth has always an objective content, the world picture and the representation (if not the interpretation) of the existence of men in a specific past epoch of time. Myth is the envelope which the men of the Biblical age have used to enclose their announcement of their understanding of life when they were confronted with the redeeming activity of God. If we are to share their understanding, we must first recognize the myth as an envelope and discard it. Then we shall be able in our contemporary and more rational age to apprehend fully the meaning of our life in the presence of the redemptive activity of God. Then the gospel may become for us today an existential message.

"As an act of redemption therefore, the cross of Christ is not a mythical symbol, but an historical fact, and a force in history which had its beginning in the historical event of the crucifixion of Jesus of Nazareth. The crucifixion is, in its historical significance, judgment upon the world and a proclamation of emancipation to men. So far as it is that, Christ is 'crucified for us'—but not in the sense of any theory of satisfaction or sacrifice. It is not to a mythological but to an historical understanding that the historic event proves itself a saving event—so far as a genuine historical understanding can comprehend an historic event in its true significance. The mythological language basically does nothing more than provide a form of expression for the significance of the historic event. The historic event of the cross has created a new historical situation by virtue of its own specific meaning. The proclamation of the cross as the act of redemption asks the hearer whether he accepts this meaning for himself; whether he will let himself be crucified with Christ." [92]

"Therefore the resurrection is not a mythical occurrence which can make the meaning of the cross believable. The resurrection is believed just as the meaning of the cross is believed. Truly, faith in the resurrection is nothing other than faith in the cross as the act of redemption, faith in the cross as the Cross of Christ. One cannot first believe in Christ and then on His cross; to believe in Christ means to believe on the cross as the Cross of Christ. The cross is not the act of redemption because it is the cross of Christ; it is the Cross of Christ because it is the act of redemption. Apart from that, it is the tragic end of a noble man." [93]

"The true Easter faith is a fully understanding faith in the word of the gospel, the faith that the proclaimed word is the true and actual word of God. The Easter event, so far as it can be called an historic event along side the crucifixion, is nothing but the rise of the belief in the risen Christ in which the message of the gospel had its beginning. The Easter event as the resurrection of Christ is not an historic event. As an historic event it is conceivable only as the Easter faith of the first disciples." [94]

"The Easter faith of the first disciples therefore does not give us a fact which we can believe in a way to remove the hazard of *our* Easter faith. Their Easter faith is itself a part of the eschatological event which is the object of our faith." [95]

We have come another step nearer to the difference between Bultmann's and Niebuhr's understanding of mythology. It is clear that since for Bultmann myth has become an immanent, time-conditioned, human mode of expression, it can have no profound significance for history nor for society as human community. With Niebuhr, myth constitutes the transcendent medium of God's voluntary turning to man and, through man, to time and to society. Myth thereby gains extraordinary significance for history (which is the totality of human activities and decisions), for it gives them new meaning by placing them immediately under the continual judgment of God and sets them in an inherent relation to God's own activity.

In myth, God punishes the rational persistence of the human lie, and shows that man is unable to gain a complete understanding of life by himself. Through myth, God socializes man; He includes the individual together with all men in His own will for community. So the mythological word of God to man shows him specifically that he is the mediating link between God and society. With Niebuhr then, myth has decisive and final social significance, and is strictly applicable to society.

But Bultmann, since he explicitly individualizes the fulfilling of life in confrontation with the proclamation of redemption, can neither see nor acknowledge this connection between myth and society. Hence he loses the sense for the significance of history and misses the new understanding of history, which Niebuhr has gained at precisely this point. Because Niebuhr is certain that man, apart from his relatedness to God which involves always the right relation to society, is incapable of a fulfillment of life or an understanding of life, history becomes for Niebuhr the evidence of this fact. He sees history as the drama of the conflicts of mutually contradictory ways of life, of two diametrically opposed concepts of life. Because history gives evidence of this conflict, it becomes important to Niebuhr. And myth as new and final medium of the divine proclamation of judgment and justification, as God's *right speaking*, acquires decisive significance as God's *setting right* man and history in the divine transcendent act of redemption.

Directly the contrary holds for Bultmann; eschatology as end of history has wholly lost its meaning since he can see in it only a mythological form of expression, accommodated to a specific historic period. Eschatology for him has been narrowed and diminished to an immanent experience which concerns the individual, so that history has lost its essential meaning as movement toward a definitive goal. History cannot be likened to a drama directed toward a denouement which gives it meaning. Eschatological event means to Bultmann only that the individual man moves from the false to the true understanding of life because he is confronted by the saving act of God in time and place in Christ.

"The mythical eschatology is basically discredited by the simple fact that the *parousia* of Christ did not, as the New Testament expected, occur immediately; world history continued and, by the consensus of intelligent opinion, will continue to proceed. Those who believe that the world as we know it will some time end, conceive its end as the result of natural development or of a catastrophe of nature and not as the mythical event described in the New Testament. And anyone who tries to interpret the New Testament myth according to scientific theories has become, like the curate in the rectory at Nöddebo,[96] a New Testament critic without knowing it. It is not the criticism arising from the view-point of natural science which is fundamental, but that which grows out of modern man's view of himself.[97]

"As He in Whom God was present and acting, through Whom

God has reconciled the world with Himself, was an actual man in history, so the word of God is not the mysterious utterance of an oracle, but the simple proclamation of the person and the fate of Jesus of Nazareth and their significance as the history of redemption. This proclamation is understandable as a phenomenon of the history of human thought and as offering in its content and ideas a possible view of the world; and yet this proclamation claims to be the eschatological word of God. The proclaimers of the message, the apostles, are men understandable in their historic humanity. The church is a socio-historical phenomenon, its growth is understandable historically and as a part of cultural history. Yet the whole is eschatological phenomenon, eschatological event." [98]

Because for Bultmann the eschatological event occurs when through the completion of the new understanding of life by men historicity becomes history, eschatology has lost the meaning given it by myth understood as the word of God, and the criterion of history given by God in myth no longer exists. Only a human criterion remains. The primary cause for this (as appears most clearly in the statements regarding myth) is that for Bultmann, faith is the complete transformation of the understanding of life, which man himself makes. For Niebuhr, the action of God which brings man out of his sinful isolation into relation with God and simultaneously into relation with society is the significant factor. Myth points toward the supra-rational and supra-historical mystery of the God-created relatedness of God to man, and through man to society. This relatedness gives both to man and to history their real status and meaning, and at the end of time it is again revealed as the unique act of God.

This is certainly not the place for a full exposition of Bultmann's thought. Such an exposition would require a much more careful and detailed presentation, and certainly the consideration of all his work. In his *Commentary on John* and in his *Theology of the New Testament*, he has said something very different and has said far more. Neither do we intend to make any general comparison of Bultmann and Niebuhr. This would demand a much wider range of investigation and would exceed the bounds of this book. On the basis of their statements about myth, we have given merely some indication of the direction such a comparison might take.

Our sole purpose was to clarify our understanding of Niebuhr's evaluation of myth by presenting the differences between two theologians who approach the same subject with wholly different pre-suppositions, by wholly different methods, and with different aims. The comparison has at least demonstrated that for Niebuhr myth is not a secondary matter which can be safely neglected on the assumption that adequate understanding is possible without it. As we now clearly recognize, Niebuhr finds in myth what is decisive and central in his own position. We have also shown how essential, in Niebuhr's judgment, is everything which pertains to the central relation—the relation of God, man and society. And we can understand that the problem of time and its relation to history must become increasingly important to him. In his treatment of myth, Niebuhr has made it clear that the relation of religion and society is the question addressed by all ages to our age.

But the side glance at Bultmann can also prove to have been worthwhile because both Niebuhr and Bultmann agree that an earnest and vigorous effort must be made if the proclamation of the word of God is to reach modern man at all. The barrier is no spurious stumbling-block, nor is it merely human repudiation of theology or of preaching in itself. Bultmann and Niebuhr agree that the modern man must understand himself anew in the light of the proclamation of the word of God before he can attain to the real meaning of his existence.

The two men are close together also in their attempt to solve this problem of theology, and it would not be difficult to present Niebuhr from his own statements as a follower of Bultmann. But that would be to ignore the fundamental and decisive difference which lies in the fact that for Bultmann the modern man, when he is confronted with the proclamation of the redeeming act of God in Christ, there and then himself completes his understanding of his life and so finishes the saving act of God as the eschatological event. Niebuhr's position is very different. For him, the self-fulfillment of man possesses no importance of its own. On the contrary, Niebuhr believes that man's continual attempt to fulfil himself is an attempt to deny the finitude and the natural limitations of his existence, and he sees it therefore as extremely dangerous and misleading. For him, the primary requirement is that man repentantly and humbly renounce every independent fulfillment, and recognize his true personality in the inner unitedness with God as his creator, preserver, judge, and redeemer—a relatedness which God Himself decreed, and from which man is led to his proper relatedness with his fellowmen in society.

"Meaning can be attributed to history only by a mythology. The modern empiricist does not escape mythological interpretations of history in his effort to avoid them. He merely insures their inadequacy by leaving their presuppositions unexamined." [99]

"An adequate mythology of history must be able to do justice to the suggestions of meaning in momentary chaos. It must be able to realize that forces which are not immediately conscious of purpose, at least not of ultimate purpose, may be used to weave meaning into the strands of history. It must not be assumed that any mythology of history can do justice to all of its detailed facts nor that it will be absolutely true in the sense that it is the only possible interpretation of all the facts. But neither can it be assumed that a science of history which disavows mythology is more accurate in its description of the detailed facts." [100]

"The Marxian mythology stands between the mythology of Christian sects and the faith of liberalism. With liberalism it emphasizes the faith in human responsibility for the historic process. . . . With the Christian sects, the Marxian realizes that historical patterns are developed not merely by those who consciously try to weave them. It knows, in other words, that history may be interpreted in terms of meaning even when the forces of history are not conscious of the end which they are achieving. Thus Marxism believes that capitalism is destroying itself by its own inherent 'contradictions' and that it is fashioning the instruments of its own destruction." [101]

"If Christianity is to survive this era of social disintegration and social rebuilding, and is not to be absorbed in or annihilated by the secularized religion of Marxism it must come to terms with the insights of Marxist mythology. There is truth in this mythology because it is more able to affirm the moral meaning in contemporary chaos than orthodox Christianity, since the latter tends to regard all history as unredeemed and unredeemable chaos. It is superior to liberal Christianity because Christian liberalism is spiritually dependent upon bourgeois liberalism and is completely lost when its neat evolutionary process toward an ethical historical goal is suddenly engulfed in a social catastrophe." [102]

We may have been somewhat surprised, after the foregoing analysis, to find Niebuhr speaking in this way of myth; and it may seem incongruous with later developments in his thinking. But we must mark accurately the beginning of his attitude to myth. He does not, like Bultmann, approach the whole problem from the point of view of New Testament exegesis. He begins where Bultmann ends, with the failure of secular history to give man a meaningful understanding of himself. Niebuhr has begun to see that contemporary society can conceive no goal which would give it direction and meaning, that history seems to have lost all significance. Further he has realized that the proletarian-Marxist interpretation of history gains its whole dynamic from the end to be achieved, and he also sees that the Marxist interpretation of history here comes very close to the early Christian mythological apocalyptic which Bultmann believes he can arbitrarily discard. Niebuhr comes to myth from society's failure to find guidance in the ambiguity of history.

From the recognition of the effect of myth upon society Niebuhr discovers the salient meaning which myth gives to history. The whole immanent-rational interpretation of history is shattered by the impossibility of understanding the present in its harsh reality and finding in the present anything which gives meaning to the whole of history. The meaning of myth for society and therefore also for history depends for Niebuhr on the way myth connects immanent history with the transcendent which alone gives the immanent meaning.

In myth Niebuhr finds revealed not only the destiny of the individual but also what is much more important and much more difficult to describe, the fate of all mankind with all its own problems—problems which up to the present have seldom been investigated. In myth, history is portrayed as divine activity and at the same time as the history of human decision for or against this revealed history of God and man in relatedness as myth presents it. In myth the meaning of human existence as well as the essence of history is revealed by God in the judgment at the end of history. Thus myth, eschatology, history and society belong together and the first two undergird, explain and direct the last two.

We have been following Niebuhr's interpretation of the intermingling in history of the separate spiritual currents of our time and their meaning in the cataclysm of our day. We shall comprehend neither his view of history nor his criticism of society nor even his understanding of man, if we do not have the patience to trace the connections and intertwinings which he has discerned in all the various attempts which have been made to solve the problem of humanity and be done with it. There is much for us to gain because Niebuhr neither abstracts nor, when he singles out a particular movement, does he over-rate its significance. He sees that real values for society can be extracted by setting the one-sided emphases against one another.

Niebuhr stands in the front rank of the few scientific thinkers who examine soberly and realistically the nature of social relations and so reach an understanding of the problems of modern society. But he becomes therefore liable to the suspicion that he is a selector whose convincingness does not equal his diagnostic keenness. His penetrating analysis at times seems to deviate from its search for essential meaning, because the two poles—starting point and goal—which give sense and force to his diagnosis and make it valid remain obscure. In Hegelian terms: Niebuhr does not move from thesis through antithesis to synthesis. We may regret this and we perhaps cannot escape a feeling of uncertainty and confusion after reading his work, but two considerations must be admitted.

First: we have come now to the point in our investigation where Niebuhr is engaged in an analysis of earlier attempts to determine the true lines of conflict in the relatedness of man to God and society. Here he examines with extraordinary discrimination the methods of obscuring the conflict and the attempts to render it harmless, and he repudiates them all.

Second: he is determined to avoid what has been the fate of so many theologians, the loss of man's dependence either on the one side to God or on the other to society. Niebuhr will not be forced to choose between the false alternatives, gospel and world; he is determined to bring them into relation to each other. He sees the two ways of destroying the union between God, man and society embodied in orthodoxy and liberalism. Orthodoxy has given up the relation of man to the world and his responsibility to it. Liberalism has believed that it could sacrifice the relation to God and man's responsibility to Him, and has tried to make the good man content with his relation to the world.

Both tendencies alike lead to secularism. The liberal, bourgeois or middle-class view-point—whichever one prefers to call it—assumes the supremacy of spirit or reason over nature, and its hope is valid only within the domain of spirit. The consequence is that the domain of nature, the realm of impulse, remains unnoticed outside the direction and control of reason, becomes autonomous and as the stronger force refuses the guidance of reason. The proletarian-naturalistic view-point on the other hand ascribes to nature immanent law, so that the achievement of world harmony is expected from the working out of natural law. With this view, dependence on the spirit can be ignored as merely a disturbing element.

It is perhaps a pity that Niebuhr employs here the concepts of nature and spirit, not only because they have been so abused by philosophers that they have become ambiguous; but also because they are not, in our opinion, sufficiently inclusive to cover the actual trends of the present day. Niebuhr, however, is not so much interested in the exact meaning of the terms as in their mutual relation. When he asserts that "the tension between spirit and nature must remain to the end of history," [103] he is thinking of the mutual relationship of the two poles, which is such that they can never coalesce, yet neither can, in time, exist wholly isolated from and independent of the other.

Niebuhr then understands the question of the relation of religion and society as a problem for religion and society in the historical situation of our day. And the key to his analysis of culture and time lies in his recognition that a connection between them exists which cannot be overlooked even in the present confusion. This connection makes it impossible for us, from fear of chaos or from a false detachment, either to refuse to see or wilfully to obscure the conflicts and confusions which we share as part of our heritage.

Hence Niebuhr sees his task to be primarily the clear mapping of these conflicts and their exact position so that his hearers may themselves raise the question of resolving the conflict, and a renewal of life may begin on the whole battle front. Man as the middle link in the chain of relatedness is unquestionably the central point of the conflict. It follows that the renewal of relatedness must start with man.

Niebuhr's interest is emphatically anthropocentric—this does not mean that his view of the world is man-centred. We shall show later that it is not. Niebuhr's anthropocentric interest aims at setting man, who is wrongly self-centred and therefore lost, again in the relatedness which includes and subordinates him and so gives him his true meaning. Only so, by accepting his proper and subordinate place in this relationship which sets him in his own station, does man come to right action and right knowledge of himself. The confusions which surround and threaten him in his attempts to solve the problem of his true relatedness are the reflected radiations of his own confusion resulting from the denial of his bond with God and society, from his sin.

"The inevitable imperfections of life and history will be borne with the greater serenity if the ego recognizes that the blind forces of nature which frustrate the spirit are in the self as well as outside it. In classical Christianity it is suggested again and again that repentance is the beginning of redemption, even that it is synonymous with redemption. This is a profound insight; for the evils and frustrations of life and history would be, in fact, unbearable if contrition did not reduce the presumptions and pretensions of the self and reveal the fact that some of the confusions from which the spirit suffers have their direct source in the chaos of the self and that others may be regarded as punishment for the sins of the self even if they have not been obviously caused by them. The consciousness of sin in classical religion is closely related to the cynic's interpretation of human nature; but it is never purely pessimistic. Classical religious faith is always saved from despair because it knows that sin is discovered by the very faith through which men catch a glimpse of the reality of spirit. Both the heights and the depths of the world of spirit are known. The knowledge of the depths within the self saves from pride, prevents a bitter criticism of the sins of others and makes a sullen rebellion against the imperfections of nature impossible; the knowledge of the heights keeps profound self-knowledge from degenerating into bitter disillusionment." [104]

IV. Sin as Man's Severance of His Relatedness to God and Society

A. The Question of Human Action

We come now to Niebuhr's book *An Interpretation of Christian Ethics.*[1] This book is based upon the preceding investigation and carries further the rejection of secular views of man and the world as misleading and inadequate. Secular interpretations of all shades, from the idealistic-liberal to the naturalistic-proletarian, end in illusion because they could not comprehend the heights and depths of man and the world. Hence they could provide neither understanding nor decisive leadership in the abrupt change from the bourgeois epoch to the technical age of the proletariat. The resultant confusion of man in his relation to society could not be corrected by the change in the historical situation for that confusion had its origin in the separation of man from the sources of religion, out of which correcting and transforming forces might have come.

Man's isolation from the source of religion is shown in the repudiation of a transcendental mythology, for the loss of which no manufactured immanent substitute mythology without evidence of truth or potency can compensate. The severance by man of the relatedness of God, man and society, with its manifest effects on man's life and action, did not leave empirical religion unscathed.

Religion sought to absolutize itself and make itself self-sufficient; it broke its connection with its source in God. The resulting petrifaction made impossible any effective effort to influence contemporary, changing society.

Just because empirical-institutional religion desired to be enclosed and centred in itself, free from the sources which direct and transform it, it split into two sections. One, the orthodox wing, froze itself fast to its dogmatic deposit of belief; its mold stiffened until the original meaning of its dogmas could not rouse it to relate the dogmas to the time. It could not reconsider formulated dogmas by relating them to their source in order to extract what in them was permanent and pertinent.

The other, the liberal wing, in its desire not to lose access to contemporary society and its thinking, and its fear of being hampered by a bond which seemed unsuited to the time, discarded its connection with the source of religion which would have preserved for religion an unlimited and predominant authority. The result was that liberal Christianity, having lost its own proper authority, attached itself much too pliantly to the view of man and the world prevalent in society at the time of the rise of liberalism. Separated from the transforming power of its source, liberalism was unable to keep pace with the changes of man and society in the contemporary break-up; still less could it move ahead as a leader. Renewal, "new birth," will happen only when religion in its empirical-institutional manifestation is again related to its source, to God; and is, in the power of that source, again able to reach man in his present situation in the changing society of his day. Then the cure of society can result from God through men who find themselves anew in their true double relatedness.

Niebuhr really proceeds farther towards the controlling aims of both orthodoxy and liberalism than either could or would go while the essential connection with their source was rejected or discarded. He ties orthodoxy in its dogmatism again to the source of religion from which those dogmas originally arose in forms suited to their time and meaningful at that time. Transformed anew by the source, these dogmas may be re-expressed and adapted to our time and our thinking. On the other hand, Niebuhr penetrates behind the inept (because out-moded and false) human image set up in liberalism and brings liberalism again to the fulfillment of its real desire, to close contact with the fundamentally changed society of the present day, without sacrificing for the sake of this contact the coexistent connection of religion to its source, a connection which is essential since it creates the only possibility for religion to serve society as a guide without losing touch with it.

Niebuhr's anthropocentric interest has not diminished. That interest remains predominant precisely because man is recognized as the connecting link between God and society. But a new emphasis, which coincides with a change in Niebuhr's theological and social thinking, begins in the work now before us, significantly a Christian ethic.

"The distinctive contribution of religion to morality lies in its comprehension of the dimension of depth in life. A secular moral act resolves the conflicts of interest and passion, revealed in any immediate situation, by whatever counsels a decent prudence may suggest, the most usual counsel being that of moderation—'in nothing too much.' A religious morality is constrained by its sense of a dimension of depth to trace every force with which it deals to some ultimate origin and to relate every purpose to some ultimate end. It is concerned not only with immediate values and disvalues, but with the problem of good and evil, not only with immediate objectives, but with ultimate hopes." [2]

These questions become acute because religion must always deal with life as a unity and with the meaning of life in all its relations. This striving for an ultimately valid relatedness forces religion both to penetrate into the depth of its source and to reach outward to the social order. But the dimension of depth always has precedence and authority. It transcends all visible given reality and leads to God. It gives direction to the question of what ought to be and what actually is.

"The Christian believes that the ideal of love is real in the will and nature of God, even though he knows of no place in history where the ideal has been realized in its pure form." [3]

This leads us to a clearer understanding of what was meant when Niebuhr spoke of the resources or the source of religion, for there the renewal, the new birth, of man's whole relatedness must originate. The source of religion marks the frontier between transcendence and immanence and so it is also the place where the word of God from the transcendent impinges on the immanent and acts upon it. For Niebuhr it is highly important that the relation of immanence to transcendence be preserved both as continuity and as tension, thus excluding both extreme dualism and pantheism. Here, as we have seen, he is guided by his ethical concern that man may come into the right relation to society. Gospel and world are to be brought into relation to each other without merging.

"The ethical fruitfulness of various types of religion is determined by the quality of their tension between the historical and the transcendent. This quality is measured by two considerations: The degree to which the transcendent truly transcends every value and achievement of history, so that no relative value of historical achievement may become the basis of moral complacency; and the degree to which the transcendent remains in organic contact with the historical, so that no degree of tension may rob the historical of its significance." [4]

We have seen already that both orthodox and liberal Christianity met this requirement as little as did liberal and naturalistic philosophy. Niebuhr finds in their common failure a reason for again showing in this context the unique significance of myth in the solution of the problem. He makes this illuminating comment:

"The religious myth, on the other hand, points to the ultimate ground of existence and its ultimate fulfillment. Therefore the great religious myths deal with creation and redemption. But since myth cannot speak of the trans-historical without using symbols and events in history as its forms of expression, it invariably falsifies the facts of history, as seen by science, to state its truth. Religion must therefore make the confession of St. Paul its own: 'As deceivers and yet true' (II Cor. 6:8). If in addition religion should insist that its mythical devices have a sacred authority which may defy the conclusions at which science arrives through its observations, religion is betrayed into deception without truth." [5]

In contrast, without the mythological word from the transcendent, modern Christianity slips into an insipid immanence where the kingdom of God is translated into a perfect society or a "United Nations," Christ into the ideal good man, and Christian love into a "counsel of prudent mutuality," without reckoning on

"the limits of the human and the temporal—in short without the suggestion of transcendence.

"Failure to recognize the heights led modern Christianity to an equal blindness toward the darker depths of life. The 'sin' of Christian orthodoxy was translated into the imperfections of ignorance, which an adequate pedagogy would soon overcome." [6]

If we are to escape such falsifications, the Christian ethic must keep itself in controlled independence from the world, not separating itself from the world, yet not merging with it. Myth makes this possible, for myth is "supra-scientific." It deals with vertical aspects of reality which transcend the horizontal relationships which science analyzes, charts and records. The classical myth refers to the transcendent source and end of existence without abstracting it from existence.

"In this sense the myth alone is capable of picturing the world as a realm of coherence and meaning without defying the facts of incoherence. Its world is coherent because all facts in it are related to some central source of meaning; but it is not rationally coherent because the myth is not under the abortive necessity of relating all things to each other in terms of immediate rational unity. The God of mythical religion is, significantly, the Creator and not the First Cause. . . . To say that God is the creator is to use an image which transcends the canons of rationality, but which expresses both his organic relation to the world and his distinction from the world. To believe that God created the world is to feel that the world is a realm of meaning and coherence without insisting that the world is totally good or that the totality of things must be identified with the Sacred." [7]

Niebuhr's assumption in beginning the discussion of a Christian ethic is then that a transcendent meaning given to the world makes such an ethic possible, and that a realistic look at the world proves it pertinent. Identification with the world and flight from the world are both excluded as equally unethical behavior. It is clear that what Niebuhr has presented as the prime necessity for man if he is to have a right relation to society is an exact replica of that which myth has to say of God: "both His organic relation to the world and His distinction from the world." So in Niebuhr's ethic, the position of man in society is conditioned and his action therein is directed by God's attitude as He turns toward the world to relate it to Himself. The word of God, ever coming to man and determining man's being, the word of God which involves man in God's own turning to society as a whole, this Niebuhr calls prophetic religion.

From all that has been said, we can easily estimate the significance which prophetic religion has for Niebuhr.

"The myth of the Creator God offers the possibilities for a prophetic religion in which the transcendent God becomes both the judge and the redeemer of the world. This possibility is, however, not an inevitability. It is always possible that a mythical religion become unduly centred in the myth of Genesis, thus glorifying the given world as sacred without subjecting its imperfections to the judgment of the Holy. In this case the result is a religion of sacramentalism rather than of prophecy. The sacramentalism of Christian orthodoxy, in which all natural things are symbols and images of the divine transcendence, but in which the tension between the present and the future of prophetic religion is destroyed, is a priestly deflation of prophetic religion. In genuinely prophetic religion the God who transcends the created world also convicts a sinful world of its iniquities and promises an ultimate redemption from them. The realm of redemption is never, as in rational and mystical religion, above the realm of living history, but within and at the end of it." [8]

We see how on the basic theme of the relation between God and society, the significant concepts, myth and prophecy, define and limit; how they express more exactly what was before presented to us more vaguely under the concepts, sources of religion and institutional religion. As myth presents the entrance of the personal revealing word of God from the transcendent to the immanent, relating God to man; so the word of the prophet is also God's reaching towards the specific situation of man in which man is limited by nature and time. Both myth and prophecy in this way represent the personal reaching out of God to men and are indispensible if man is to be really united to his God. Every diminution or reduction to mere symbolism interrupts this personal turning of God to man (of the transcendent to the immanent), robs man of the uniqueness of his true position in the world, and robs history of its meaning and goal. With a faked religion, which in its "deflation" and destructiveness sacramentalism actually is, true humanity is made impossible.

Here we learn what sin means in this context—what it always in the deepest sense means for Niebuhr—the breaking of relatedness to God. The destruction of the human being and of true community in society follows this break and is inseparable from it. Sin has its deepest roots in selfish, self-centred religiosity which instead of serving God and neighbor perverts and narrows religion itself in order to use it for self-glorification. With this perverted religion, prophecy is constantly at war.

"A vital prophetic Christianity is consequently forced not only to maintain its independence against naturalism and other-worldliness, but to preserve its purity against sacramental vitiations of its own basic prophetic mythology. The inclination of Christianity to deviate from prophetic religion in terms of sacramental complacency on the one hand and mystic other-worldliness on the other is partly derived from the Greek influence upon its thought and is partly the consequence of its own commendable sharpening of the religious tension in prophetic religion. The religion of Jesus is prophetic religion in which the moral ideal of love and vicarious suffering, elaborated by the second Isaiah, achieves such purity that the possibility of its realization in history becomes remote. His kingdom of God is always a possibility in history, because its heights of pure love are organically related to the experience of love in all human life, but it is also an impossibility in history and always beyond every historical achievement. Men living in nature and in the body will never be capable of the sublimation of egoism and the attainment of the sacrificial passion, the complete disinterestedness which the ethic of Jesus demands. The social justice which Amos demanded represented a possible ideal for society. Jesus' conception of pure love is related to the idea of justice as the holiness of God is related to the goodness of men. It transcends the possible and the historical. Perhaps this is the reason why the eschatology of later prophecy had ceased to be as unambiguously this-worldly as was that of early prophecy." [9]

The tension in prophetic religion and in the religion of Jesus Christ Niebuhr sees as the result of the constant invasion of historical immanence from the side of transcendence. Man cannot be satisfied in his world and in time; he stands always under the compulsion to undertake what goes beyond the possibilities of space and time. Man's relation to God through religion compels him towards the fulfillment in society of the command of love as given by God and realized in Jesus Christ. Such fulfillment is wholly beyond the power of man in separation from God. But man's self-will constantly fights this tension, and religion is therefore always in danger from the temptation to put an end to the tension by admitting only immanence.

"A vital Christian faith and life is thus under the necessity of perennially preserving its health against the peril of diseases and corruptions arising out of its own life; and of protecting itself against errors to which non-mythical religions tempt it. Most of its own weaknesses arise when the mythical paradoxes of its faith are resolved; most of the perils from the outside come from the pessimism and dualism of mystical and rational religion.

"Only a vital Christian faith, renewing its youth in its prophetic origin, is capable of dealing adequately with the moral and social problems of our age; only such a faith can affirm the significance of temporal and mundane existence without capitulating unduly to the relativities of the temporal process. Such a faith alone can point to a source of meaning which transcends all the little universes of value and meaning which 'have their day and cease to be' and yet not seek refuge in an eternal world where all history ceases to be significant. Only such a faith can outlast the death of old cultures and the birth of new civilizations, and yet deal in terms of moral responsibility with the world in which cultures and civilizations engage in struggles of death and life." [10]

The Christian ethic which results from these assumptions must be, Niebuhr believes, founded on and conformed to the ethic of Jesus; and he now turns to the consideration of that ethic as he understands it.

"The ethic of Jesus is the perfect fruit of prophetic religion. Its ideal of love has the same relation to the facts and necessities of human experience as the God of prophetic faith has to the world. It is drawn from, and relevant to, every moral experience. It is immanent in life as God is immanent in the world. It must, therefore, be confused neither with the ascetic ethic of world-denying religions nor with the prudential morality of naturalism, designed to guide good people to success and happiness in this world." [11]

"The ethic of Jesus does not deal at all with the immediate moral problem of every human life—the problem of arranging some kind of armistice between various contending factions and forces. It has nothing to say about the relativities of politics and economics, nor of the necessary balances of power which exist and must exist in even the most intimate social relationships. The absolutism and perfectionism of Jesus' love ethic sets itself uncompromisingly not only against the natural self-regarding impulses, but against the necessary prudent defenses of the self, required because of the egoism of others. It does not establish a connection with the horizontal points of a political or social ethic or with the diagonals which a prudential individual ethic draws between the moral ideal and the facts of a given situation. It has only a vertical dimension between the loving will of God and the will of man.

"Love as the quintessence of the character of God is not established by argument, but taken for granted." [12]

For Niebuhr, the character of God is revealed in His love, that is in His full, dynamic, personal turning to men. It is important for us to recognize that the ethic based on this conviction can never in any way whatever be allowed to become, like the ethic of moralism, depersonalized into a set of maxims, a tool which sinful man relying on himself alone could use to master his relation to his environment. The fundamental character of Niebuhr's theology is misapprehended if we are unwilling to see that for him the ethic of Jesus cannot be related directly to the facts of world and society, but applies exclusively to man himself.

Man as the connecting link in the relatedness of God to society is indispensible; man is the place where the love of God imparts to man's objective world a meaning truly personal. But this means that the ethic of Jesus, in contrast to all secular ethic, cannot be separated from the person who is acting and be made universal. "It has only a vertical dimension between the loving will of God and the will of man." So both parts of the expression of God's will to love are equally important and are inseparable. The love of God is the dynamic in the will of God, and God's will therefore is always motivated by love and always acts personally, for love admits no relation except the personal. Also the point of contact between God and man is the will of man. Man's will responds to God's will to love—or it does not respond. Here recurs the Biblical concept of sin. The Christian ethic is therefore concerned with the personal will of men.

"The contrast in prophetic religion is not between perfection and imperfection, or between the temporal and the eternal, but between good and evil will. But since the evil will of man is not the consequence of pure finiteness, the life of man is not without symbols and echoes of the divine." [13]

We must now turn, since the nature of the relation between God and man has been made clear, to the second pole of the relatedness, to man; and we must consider especially the will of man as the point where contact in the relatedness to God is made or lost. The will of man is created and determined by relatedness to God. This must be recognized clearly and without qualification. Only because of the divine creative will for relatedness, do human wills, free and hence creative, exist at all. The desire for relatedness is the nature of personality. From this desire, human (in distinction to animal) activity springs, and from this desire alone can the uniqueness of the human being be understood. This specific point will engage our attention later; here we need only say that the ethic of Jesus involves the recognition of the unique character of human relatedness and its precariousness. The ethic of Jesus reveals the whole force of the tension within that relatedness. Later we shall have reason to see more clearly the nature of the breaking of this relatedness in tension.

"The very basis of self-love is the natural will to survive. In man the animal impulse to maintain life becomes an immediate temptation to assert the self against the neighbor. Therefore, in the ethic of Jesus, concern for physical existence is prohibited: 'Take no thought for your life, what ye shall eat, or what ye shall drink; nor yet for your body, what ye shall put on.' "[14]

"The most natural expansion of the self is the expansion through possessions. Therefore the love of possessions as a form of self-assertion meets the same uncompromising rigor. 'Lay not up for yourselves treasures upon earth . . . for where your treasure is, there will your heart be also.' "[15]

"The most penetrating analysis of the character of self-love is to be found in Jesus' excoriation of pride, particularly the pride of good people. Pride is a subtle form of self-love. It feeds, not on the material advantages which more greedy people seek, but upon social approval . . . [Jesus'] strictures against the Pharisees were partly directed against their social pride. 'All their works they do for to be seen of men . . . and love the uppermost rooms at feasts and the chief seats in the synagogues and greetings in the markets and to be called of men, Rabbi, Rabbi.' "[16]

Another point must be settled before the application of the ethic of Jesus can be clearly understood and the nature of the destruction of the relatedness of God, man and society by sin be demonstrated. The activity of God's love is not completed in man nor in society nor even in history, but only in the fulfilling annulment of history at "the end of the days." Self-satisfaction is unattainable by man here, and his persistent pursuit of it reveals the destructiveness of sin.

"There is . . . an eschatological element in, and even basis for, the ethic of Jesus. The ethical demands made by Jesus are incapable of fulfillment in the present existence of man. They proceed from a transcendent and divine unity of essential reality, and their final fulfillment is possible only when God transmutes the present chaos of this world into its final unity. . . . Placing the final fulfillment at the end of time and not in a realm above temporality is to remain true to the genius of prophetic religion and to state mythically what cannot be stated rationally. If stated rationally the world is divided between the temporal and the eternal and only the eternal forms above the flux of temporality have significance. To state the matter mythically is to do justice to the fact that the eternal can only be fulfilled in the temporal." [17]

The significance thus given to eschatology must be considered carefully. Niebuhr emphasizes a two-fold meaning. First, eschatology gives meaning to history since history's fulfillment is to be found in the *Eschaton* as the event which ends history, and not in a realm of ideas above history. Second, on the other hand, eschatology prevents history (that which is temporal) from being accepted as meaningful in itself; its fulfillment is given to it from beyond history and this fulfillment is at the same time a judgment upon it.

"Apocalypticism in terms of a specific interpretation of history may thus be regarded as the consequence and not the cause of Jesus' religion and ethic. The apocalypse is a mythical expression of the impossible possibility under which all human life stands. The Kingdom of God is always at hand in the sense that impossibilities are really possible, and lead to new actualities in given moments of history. Nevertheless, every actuality of history reveals itself, after the event, as only an approximation of the ideal; and the Kingdom of God is therefore not here. It is in fact always coming but not here.

"The historical illusions which resulted inevitably from this mythical statement of the situation in which the human spirit finds itself do not destroy the truth in the myth; no more than the discovery that the fall of man was not actual history destroys the mythical truth in the story of the fall. Nevertheless it must be admitted that the ethical rigor of the early church was maintained through the hope of the second coming of Christ and the establishment of his Kingdom. When the hope of the *parousia* waned the rigor of the Christian ethic was gradually dissipated and the Church, forced to come to terms with the relativities of politics and economics and the immediate necessities of life, made unnecessary compromises with these relativities which frequently imperiled the very genius of prophetic religion. But the mistakes which resulted, both from illusions about the course of history and from the adjustments which had to be made when the illusion vanished, do not invalidate the basic insights of prophetic religion. They merely present Christian ethics afresh with the problem of compromise, the problem of creating and maintaining tentative harmonies of life in the world on terms of the possibilities of the human situation, while yet at the same time preserving the indictment upon all human life of the impossible possibility, the law of love." [18]

Niebuhr asserts definitely (and we should not ignore his assertion) that the ideal of love and the law of love is an "impossible possibility" for man. Man can neither qualify the absolute love command of the ethic of Jesus nor can he of himself at all fulfil it. It is never a possibility within his grasp on which he can pride himself. It directs him continually toward a necessary and redemptive adherence to God. But in such adherence, the command is a possibility specifically designated for him and becoming actual through him. The absolute love commandment in the ethic of Jesus is for man a perpetual signpost pointing to the direction in which God wills to work through man, toward his fellowmen and so toward society. But it also shows immutably that fulfillment lies beyond history in the *Eschaton*.

We have come at length to the question of evil as the destruction by man of the relatedness of God, man and the world—to the question of sin.

"The full dimension of human life includes not only an impossible ideal, but realities of sin and evil which are more than simple imperfections and which prove that the ideal is something more than the product of a morbidly sensitive religious fantasy.

Anything less than perfect love in human life is destructive of life. All human life stands under an impending doom because it does not live by the law of love. Egoism is always destructive. The wages of sin is death. The destruction of our contemporary civilization through its injustice and through the clash of conflicting national wills is merely one aspect and one expression of the destruction of sin in the world.

"Confronted with this situation humanity always faces a double task. The one is to reduce the anarchy of the world to some kind of immediately sufferable order and unity; and the other is to set these tentative and insecure unities and achievements under the criticism of the ultimate ideal. When they are not thus challenged, what is good in them becomes evil and each tentative harmony becomes the cause of new anarchy. With Augustine we must realize that the peace of the world is gained by strife. That does not justify us either in rejecting such tentative peace or in accepting it as final. The peace of the city of God can use and transmute the lesser and insecure peace of the city of the world; but that can be done only if the peace of the world is not confused with the ultimate peace of God." [19]

It is noteworthy that Niebuhr, who once in Detroit faced with "the brutal facts of life in a great industrial center" had doubted the applicability and power of the traditional Christianity of his student days, shows now a sensitivity for the social effects of sin which influences his thinking decisively. He is incapable of satisfying himself in the usual theological fashion by defining sin as a matter between man and God, admitting that it has certain results in man's relations with his fellowmen, but assuming that such results are not theologically important. Niebuhr holds firmly to "the prophetic in religion." In its light he understands clearly the "vertical dimension" of the message of Jesus, and he knows that it cannot be applied directly, as moral teaching, to man's relation to his environment. It is exclusively personal. Because Niebuhr takes absolutely seriously the whole depth of the love of God and sets it rightly in close, inseparable connection with life itself, sin is for him a question of life and death. Egoism and the injustice resulting from it, he recognizes as totally destructive.

In every place and in every act where he sees this self-destruction of men, carrying with it the destruction of all things, he will not relax his effort to uncover this destructive force and make it plainly evident. Men demonstrate their sin precisely by their unreadiness to recognize the injustice and chaos of civilization as sin.

It is clear that it is as incorrect to see in Niebuhr only a critic of societies and cultures as to think that he is only a dogmatic theologian. It is the living turning of God to society in the world, understood as God's act of love creating life, which leads him to reflect unweariedly upon the breaking of this relation by man, its connecting link, and which makes the problem of sin for him the chief question of theology. The central chapter of the book now before us is therefore that which deals with the Christian view of sin. It begins by presenting an important contrast.

"In liberal Christianity there is an implicit assumption that human nature has the resources to fulfill what the gospel demands. The Kantian axiom, 'I ought, therefore I can,' is accepted as basic to all analyses of the moral situation. In classical Christianity the perfectionism of the gospel stands in a much more difficult relation to the estimate of human resources. The love commandment stands in juxtaposition to the fact of sin. It helps, in fact, to create the consciousness of sin." [20]

But such a juxtaposition is impossible where life and action have a merely immanent meaning; it is possible only where they receive direction from beyond the immanent.

"In prophetic religion the flux of the finite world is both a revelation and a veiling of the eternal creative principle and will. Every finite event points to something beyond itself in two directions, to a source from which it springs and an end to which it moves. Prophetic religion believes, in other words, in a God who is both the creator and the fulfillment of life.

"The human spirit is set in this dimension of depth in such a way that it is able to apprehend, but not to comprehend the total dimension. . . . [The] human reason is itself imbedded in the passing flux, a tool of a finite organism, the instrument of its physical necessities, and the prisoner of the partial perspectives of a limited time and place. . . .

"This paradoxical relation of finitude and infinity, and consequently of freedom and necessity, is the mark of the uniqueness of the human spirit in this creaturely world. Man is the only mortal animal who knows that he is mortal, a fact which proves that in some sense he is not mortal. Man is the only creature imbedded in the flux of finitude who knows that this is his fate; which proves that in some sense this is not his fate. Thus when life is seen in its total dimension, the sense of God and the sense of sin are involved in the same act of self-consciousness; for to be self-conscious is to see the self as a finite object separated from essential reality; but also related to it, or there could be no knowledge of separation. If this religious feeling is translated into moral terms it becomes the tension between the principle of love and the impulse of egoism, between the obligation to affirm the ultimate unity of life and the urge to establish the ego against all competing forms of life." [21]

These statements contain the heart of Niebuhr's anthropology. It will be further developed and details added, but with no essential change. We should note that this formulation is found in connection with the question of sin. This means two things: Niebuhr is not interested in man in himself, neither in the ideal man, nor in the creature man as he may appear in the abstract. He is interested in man in his double relation to God and to society. When he looks at man in this relation, his eye is sharpened to perceive that to see man in this relation is to see him standing actually in a broken relation which destroys him. This perception brings Niebuhr to the centre of his conception of man.

But also Niebuhr recognizes that the knowledge of sin and sin's destructiveness could not arise from man himself without any reference to God. He never explains sin from man's side alone—quite the contrary. He investigates the nature of sin more deeply than is usual among theologians in order that its effects on man's relation to society may appear more clearly and that consequently the sinful maneuvers of men in their attempts to camouflage their sins may be made impossible. If these two mutually qualifying points are not clearly seen, injustice is done to Niebuhr and the main line of his thought is not understood.

But Niebuhr does not stop here: "The Christian approach to the problem of sin is, however, not exhausted in the recognition of mere finiteness." [22]

The fact that Niebuhr not only goes further but goes further in just this way shows clearly that he cannot view the consciousness of sin as an achievement of the inner man. Mary F. Thelen's investigation of sin in contemporary American theology—in itself a scholarly study—comes to no acceptable conclusion on Niebuhr because at this point she did not see clearly and failed to grasp his thought as a whole.[23]

"The particular virtue of the myth of the Fall is that it does justice to the paradoxical relation of spirit and nature in human evil. In the religious thought which flows from its interpretation, reason and consciousness are not the unqualified instruments of good and the manifestations of the divine. Neither is the body or material existence evil as such. . . . According to the myth of the Fall, evil came into the world through human responsibility. It was neither ordained in the counsels of God nor the inevitable consequence of temporal existence. Both the monistic and dualistic pitfalls of consistence philosophy are thus avoided, at the price, of course, of leaving the metaphysical problem at loose ends. The origin of evil is attributed to an act of rebellion on the part of man. Responsibility for the evil which threatens the unity of existence is laid upon mankind, but this responsibility is slightly qualified by the suggestion that man was tempted. The serpent, symbol of the principle of evil, in the story of the Fall does justice to the idea that human rebellion is not the first cause and source of evil in the world. The world was not a perfect harmony even before human sin created confusion. The idea in Hebrew mythology that Satan is both a rebel against God and yet ultimately under his dominion, expresses the paradoxical fact that on the one hand evil is something more than the absence of order, and on the other that it depends upon order. There can be disorder only in an integrated world; and the forces of disorder can be effective only if they are themselves ordered and integrated. Only a highly cohesive nation can offer a threat to the peace of the world. Thus the devil is possible only in a world controlled by God and can be effective only if some of the potencies of the divine are in him. Evil, in other words, is not the absence but the corruption of good. . . . In such a mythical conception evil is more positive than in monistic philosophies, and more dependent upon the good than in religious and philosophical dualisms. The myth of the Fall is thus in harmony with the mixture of profound pessimism and ultimate optimism which distinguishes prophetic religion from other forms of faith and other world-views. In the faith of prophetic religion existence is more certainly meaningful, its meaning is more definitely threatened by evil, and the triumph of good over evil is ultimately more certain than in alternative forms of religion." [24]

Only the faith of prophetic religion in its paradoxical relation and its tension does justice to the paradoxical relation of spirit and nature in human evil. Niebuhr emphasizes in the myth of the Fall the preservation of this tension to the full and the refusal to lessen it in any way, because he sees in every attempt at evasion an error which in the history of theology and philosophy has invariably resulted in a conception of sin which no longer corresponds to the truth.

Where this happens, where transcendent myth no longer points the way to the understanding of sin, there cannot be true confession of sin. Neither the heavy burden of sin nor the responsibility for sin is admitted when the existing tension is prematurely and wrongly loosened. All such efforts are at bottom attempts to excuse man so that he might no longer need divine redemption since there would no longer be cause for judgment. Prophetic religion asserts the contrary.

"Prophetic religion attributes moral evil to an evil will rather than to the limitations of natural man. The justification for such an emphasis lies in the fact that human reason is actually able to envisage moral possibilities, more inclusive loyalties, and more adequate harmonies of impulse and life in every instance of moral choice than those which are actually chosen. There is, therefore, an element of perversity, a conscious choice of the lesser good, involved in practically every moral action; and certainly there are some actions in which this conscious perversity is the dominant force of the action." [25]

Although it is important to maintain that both reason and impulse are included as factors in sin, the emphasis must be upon the will. It is the will which chooses; and the will becomes the definitive bearer of the choice of sin. Sin cannot be ascribed to impulse alone or to reason alone; it originates at the point where these unite in an act of will. Sin abides in the will where impulse and reason meet, exactly where lies also the point of contact in the relationship with God. This conjunction can hardly be accidental.

"According to the prophetic conception, moral evil lies at the juncture of nature and spirit. The reality of moral guilt is asserted because the forces and impulses of nature never move by absolute necessity, but under and in the freedom of the spirit. But the myth of the Fall involves more than this assertion of moral responsibility. It involves a definition of, or at least clues to, the character of moral evil in man. Sin is rebellion against God. If finiteness cannot be without guilt because it is mixed with freedom and stands under ideal possibilities, it cannot be without sin (in the more exact sense of the term) because man makes pretensions of being absolute in his finiteness. He tries to translate his finite existence into a more permanent and absolute form of existence. Ideally men seek to subject their arbitrary and contingent existence under the dominion of absolute reality. But practically they always mix the finite with the eternal and claim for themselves, their nation, their culture, or their class the centre of existence. This is the root of all imperialism in man and explains why the restricted predatory impulses of the animal world are transmuted into the boundless imperial ambitions of human life. Thus the moral urge to establish order in life is mixed with the ambition to make oneself the centre of that order; and devotion to every transcendent value is corrupted by the effort to insert the interests of the self into that value. The organizing centre of life and history must transcend life and history, since everything which appears in time and history is too partial and incomplete to be its centre. But man is destined, both by the imperfection of his knowledge and by his desire to overcome his finiteness, to make absolute claims for his partial and finite values. He tries, in short, to make himself God.

"This explanation of the matter not only emphasizes the spiritual, rather than natural, character of human evil, but also involves the doctrine of its inevitability. The most ideal aspirations of the human spirit always contain an alloy of idealizing pretensions. The higher the aspirations rise the more do sinful pretensions accompany them." [26]

Niebuhr thus repudiates all attempts to exclude in any way whatever from man's sinful rebellion against God a spiritual realm or an ideal will. Because sin is rebellion in the perverted self-centred will, sin can never be separated from the will of man. As little as any decision or act can be severed from living relation to God, so little can the moment of sinful rebellion against God be eliminated from any act in which man wills to establish himself in his self-will and depart from dependence upon God. But this insight does not mean that Niebuhr accepts with the followers of Augustine and Luther the total depravity of man.

"The human capacity for self-transcendence, the ability to see beyond an immediate world to more and more inclusive loyalties and values, is the basis of all that is good and all that is evil in human life. If it were altogether evil and corrupt, it could not become the basis of the kind of evil for which men feel themselves responsible. It is human freedom, in other words, created by the transcendence of reason over impulse, which makes sin possible. Therefore, if man is totally corrupt he is not sinful at all. At any rate, sin has been stripped of the connotation of guilt, or guilt has been divested of the implication of moral responsibility.

"On this important problem Augustinian Christianity and modern culture have both failed to grasp the paradoxical relation of spirit and nature, of reason and impulse, in human wrong-doing. The former fails to make a significant distinction between reason and impulse and the latter erroneously sees in reason the unqualified basis of virtue and in impulse the root of all evil. The former theory obscures the fact that a significant portion of human wrong-doing is due to human finiteness. This finiteness includes both the imperfect vision of human reason and the blindness of human impulse." [27]

"In modern culture, on the other hand, the unqualified identification of reason and virtue has led to untold evils and confusions. Against the illusions of modern culture it must be maintained that the natural impulses of life are not so anarchic and reason is not so unqualifiedly synthesizing as has been assumed." [28]

When Niebuhr so decisively maintains the freedom of man, it must be clear that his formulation of the problem is wholly unlike the many unfruitful theological and philosophical discussions on the freedom of the human will. He can never allow the freedom of the will to be denied *a priori* to man as such, nor assume that the question has been settled so that man—at least *de facto*—can never be faced with his responsibility. Nor can he admit that the question of man's will is already decided in the anthropological definition of man. Niebuhr sees the nature of sin precisely in the fact that man unavoidably but not of necessity denies his dependence on God. Sin therefore to Niebuhr is not an inner quality of man's being; it is rather a decision of the whole man determining his outward action. It is a problem of relationship in the personal "I-Thou" relation.

Niebuhr is not interested in man as such (if there be any such thing) nor in man's capability or incapability apart from his immediate environment. He inquires only where and why man stands as he does and not otherwise in his relation to God and society; whether that position is really inherent in his nature and inevitable, or whether help and redemption are possible for him where he stands. We therefore must not do what Niebuhr rightly and wisely does not do, construct an abstract problem concerning the freedom of the will. Niebuhr himself is concerned primarily for the visible consequences of the various theories propounded rather than desirous of reasoning them out logically. (The latter effort is certainly unfruitful and ultimately, for sound reasons, impossible.)

Now while the Augustinian and Lutheran view of man's total depravity can lead, because of a resultant determinism, to unqualified pessimism and to quietism so that no place is left for adequate social education; modern culture, under-estimating the power of impulse and over-estimating that of reason, has led to the blocking of the possibility that man may achieve order in his life, in society and in the world. Niebuhr himself recognizes that in developing a Christian ethic it is no easy task to steer without loss between the Scylla and Charybdis of these two dangers.

"Naturally, it is not easy to elaborate an adequate ethic for the immediate social problems of human existence in terms of the tension created by Christian love perfectionism on the one hand, and this kind of realism on the other." [29]

But exactly this is what Niebuhr sees as the task of the Christian ethic. And it is at this point that we see most clearly his characteristic postulates: man is the point of contact in the relation of God and society; it is the driving force of the love coming from God to man which makes man capable of seeing the realities of life as they are; in exactly the same way (Niebuhr asserts this explicitly) by which man gained this realistic view of the world, there can come to him restoration of the broken relatedness, annulment of sin.

In the rest of the book we are discussing, Niebuhr forcibly combats in detail the errors set forth above. Against the illusions of liberal culture, he shows that the true nature of man, which liberal culture was as unwilling as it was unable to see clearly, makes it absolutely impossible for man in any given situation to fulfil the love command as its stands in the ethic of Jesus. Without regard to the true nature of man, the situation cannot be known for what it actually is. The love command becomes valid for man only when he fully recognizes his own inability to fulfil it, so that the commandment becomes for him "the impossible possibility," as Niebuhr so often calls it. Then man ceases to try to buttress his own righteousness, then he opens himself wholly and unconditionally to the love of God which radically transforms him.

The final chapter of the book deals with love as forgiveness; that is, with the restoration of man's relatedness to God, which was destroyed by sin and is to be created anew. Then is created also a new relation of man to society, replacing the distorted and destructive relation which is the result of sin.

An explicit *but* opposes the consequences of the orthodox doctrine of total depravity embodied in pessimism and quietism.

Since it is the love of God which creates man anew, man is driven beyond himself—not however into Promethean self-transcendence. The guilt of that kind of self-exaltation by which man has always sought, in opposition to the love of God, to escape his confining limitations is clearly manifest in social, economic and political injustice. In contrast, man in his renewed relatedness to God gives himself to the service of his fellowmen; and only such service can make possible true community of men in society.

Niebuhr indeed knows that *Caritas* (charity, love) in the individual sense has always been practiced in orthodoxy. He is as far as possible from wishing to reduce the personal specific force of love for individuals to a shallow romantic-idealistic universalism or a bureaucratic uniformity. In a special chapter he treats of the nature of individual love and differentiates it from the application of the love commandment to politics and economics, concerning which he had been critical. However, he rightly rejects the view that love ceases to act in the area of society, of the "world" so-called. On the contrary, love establishes a new centre within a society which has become disoriented and without middle point. That centre is man loved by God, transformed by God's love, and therefore newly and more closely bound to society in the relation of love. At that centre, the love of God impinging on man both radiates from him and is reflected by him.

Niebuhr feels that he must clearly differentiate his position here from that of Emil Brunner, but he has mistaken a difference in emphasis for a fundamental divergence. At bottom the meaning and aim of both are the same. Both defend themselves against the misconception that human love, created and made possible by the love of God, can be applied as an abstract principle in non-personal areas. Both realize that love bears a purely personal character. Niebuhr has magnified a mere difference of emphasis into disagreement. The presupposition of all Brunner's discussion of righteousness [30] is the personality of man, recognized as the creation of God. When he speaks of righteousness, therefore, it is on the assumption that what he says applies only to man so understood.

Love is implicitly included, for without love humanity is impossible. Righteousness then is first of all the willingness, possible only to a loving person, that one's fellowman should really have his due.

Niebuhr actually has the same conception. But he is so deeply concerned for the relation of man to his fellowman and even to his non-personal environment that he insists on making the explicit statement that there cannot be a neuter righteousness, apart from acting in love. He emphasizes most (what Brunner would never dispute) that it is turning in love toward one's fellows which makes it possible to see one's neighbor truly and so makes it possible to do him justice. And he feels it even more necessary to assert explicitly that there is not and cannot be any area whatever where man does not require loving relatedness to God in order to do "righteousness" in Brunner's sense of the word. In society especially, Niebuhr would never allow validity to a neuter, non-personal principle. Wherever a group or an institution of society becomes impersonal, or is stamped by an impersonal relation to others outside it, Niebuhr scents depersonalization, flight from responsibility. There he sees the personal relatedness to God already threatened by the closing of the only channel through which renewing creative power can flow from the source of religion and turn society into a truly human—that is for Niebuhr into a truly loving—community.

To put the difference of emphasis briefly: Brunner, to avoid false sentimentality, asserts that love cannot be an impersonal rule governing impersonal decisions. Niebuhr, guarding against the loss of any fragment from the arching bridge of the personal relatedness of God and society, insists on emphasizing that all righteousness is created and preserved by this relatedness conditioned by love. Figuratively expressed: Brunner maintains that a Christian shoemaker makes, not Christian shoes but good shoes. Niebuhr emphasizes that it is a Christian shoemaker who makes really good shoes.

Here at the end of our survey of Niebuhr's discussion of ethics we can perhaps consider the question which we left open earlier. At what point and for what reasons did Niebuhr substitute for the concept *religion* an expression more consonant with revelation? If we have followed carefully the preceding exposition and especially the passages quoted, we have not failed to notice that instead of the earlier use of the term *religion* in a general sense, he now uses it in two contrasting ways. He speaks of prophetic or Christian-prophetic religion and sets this over against religion in general, or other religions.

Since we have learned to know Niebuhr's understanding of prophetic religion and the high valuation he attaches to the words of the prophets, and have noticed how closely this connects with his interpretation of myth, it will not seem surprising but entirely consistent that the concept of *faith* becomes ever more important to Niebuhr. (Later a fuller inquiry must be made as to how and why faith with Niebuhr must be understood as voluntary, personal affirmation of man's station in communion with God and his fellowmen.) Niebuhr's change of terminology is noted here for the light it throws on the inner development of his theological understanding.

In this development, he was strongly influenced by an intensive study of the dialectical theology of the continent, which certainly, although he does not explicitly say so, impressed him deeply. This influence will be discussed at the end of our investigation.

B. Man's Position Between Time and Eternity

The preceding inquiry into human behavior has proved that the real problem of human life is sin. And it has also demonstrated that man's peril and failure as well as his restoration are intimately bound up with and contingent upon his position as mediating link between God and society. Niebuhr proceeds to the investigation of the theological significance of this conclusion.

We have so far established only that the relatedness of man to God is fundamental and determinative, and that it requires absolutely the relatedness of man to his fellowmen in society, and alters this relation according to its own claim. Thus the disorders of the human community result from the break in the relatedness of God and man; and the restoration of community can proceed, according to Niebuhr, only from a renewed relatedness of God and man.

It may at first strike us as strange that when Niebuhr wishes to carry further the theological investigation he encounters immediately the problem of the relation of man to time and eternity. But this is the problem to which we must turn when we consider the volume entitled *Beyond Tragedy*[31] a collection of "sermonic essays," as Niebuhr calls them. The book is an important milestone in the development of Niebuhr's thinking and presents the beginnings of ideas which he will later elaborate and systematize.

We must first recognize that Niebuhr is resolved to be more orthodox than the orthodox fundamentalist. He is determined to give to "true doctrine" its proper authority, and he seeks to bring it out of its present rigidity into life-giving conjunction with its source. Then the content, vitally renewed, will break through the temporally conditioned formulas in which it was first expressed and present its message anew in terms suited to our time. Men can then recognize its living force and will be guided by it to a new and valid relation to society.

Niebuhr himself has at times described the development of his thought as moving theologically more and more to the right, that is to the side of orthodoxy; and socially more and more to the left, that is toward socialism. This double shift was the result of his determination to understand both orthodoxy and socialism in their genuine and original intention, and of the ensuing recognition that they stand in a close mutual relation.

More and more the relation between God and man seemed to Niebuhr a relatedness which is both existent and full of tension, profoundly affecting man at every moment of his life. Religion does not exist for its own sake; it manifests itself in its function of service. Man, when he is newly related as a responsible person to God, can fulfil his responsibility only when his own life participates in God's loving activity toward men through actions motivated by his own loving concern for his fellowmen. The true function of man in society first becomes possible when the love of God is understood as seeking man where he actually is, a member of a society broken into fragments, where community relation is impossible.

This insight shattered for Niebuhr all liberal secular images of man, all illusions about man which never admit his real nature. The discovery of the true reality condemned and abolished all false solutions with their trivial inadequacy, and made room for the true solution, the restoration of man as a new creature in his true relatedness to society.

Niebuhr therefore shows convincingly the error of the current opinion that true piety is alive only in orthodoxy and true world service is to be found only in liberalism. The contrary of that superficial assumption is equally false. The true piety of orthodoxy leads to brotherliness in actual social and economic difficulties, and the true world service of liberalism is forced to realize that the difficulties of men in the world cannot be solved without a living relatedness to God.

Certainly it was Niebuhr's burning concern for men which led him to oppose every human attempt at self-justification in narrow orthodox religion and every self-complacent liberal concept of society. He recognized that all such efforts merely deepen and complicate the disturbance and division in the relation of God and society. He is intent on extending the lines of man's double relatedness to its two poles—to the living and true God and to society in its chaos. Only then does the meaning of every word in the saying of John 3:16 become clear: "God so loved the world, that he gave his only begotten Son, that whosoever believeth in him should not perish, but have everlasting life."

We shall not go wrong if we interpret Niebuhr—at least the Niebuhr of this book and of his later work—in the light of his great, almost child-like wonder at the import of this often unheeded presupposition of all Christian preaching. We shall then understand the blazing horror with which he looks upon the chaos and ruin of human community. He feels deeply that when confronted by this unique subversive incursion of God into the chaotic and ruined world—not to destroy it but to save it—all human substitute solutions and all the religions of self-rescue are catastrophically destructive.

Niebuhr may well be compared with John the Baptist, who, confronted by the bearer and guarantor of the incoming kingdom of heaven, vehemently proclaimed a message which pilloried especially the representatives of perverted and self-centred religious practices. It is well to remember here what Niebuhr himself said of his own beginning. His aim was not to heighten the conflict between gospel and world, but to bring the two together as closely as possible. But this aim did not allow him to cease his inexorable demolition of all barriers which prevent the bringing together of gospel and world.

In the introduction to the book with which we are now engaged, he says:

"The chapters of this book are sermonic essays elaborating one theme in various aspects. The theme is Christianity's dialectical conception of the relation of time and eternity, of God and the world, of nature and grace. It is the thesis of these pages that the biblical view of life is dialectical because it affirms the meaning of history and of man's natural existence on the one hand, and on the other insists that the centre, source and fulfilment of history lie beyond history.

"Christianity must therefore speak both a 'yes' and a 'no' to naturalistic philosophies. It affirms them inasfar as they insist on the meaningfulness of historical existence. It refutes them inasfar as they believe that the temporal process explains and fulfils itself. In the same way it affirms the distinction between time and eternity in mysticism, and rational dualistic philosophies, but rejects their denial of the significance of the historical process. In the biblical view each moment of history stands under and in eternity but neither exhausts nor fulfils the eternal.

"Inasfar as orthodox Christianity has developed this biblical view into a supernaturalism which conceives of two discrete realms of being, the natural and the supernatural, it represents a petrifaction of a more mythical and dialectical biblical thought. It may not be unjust to regard this development as the consequence of Greek rationalism upon the more mythical and Hebraic biblical thought, in which the depth of eternity in time is conceived of in terms which sacrifice rational consistency to profundity of religious insight. . . .

"The idea of a meaningful history does not, however, explain the actual content of meaning. It is the thesis of these essays that the Christian view of history passes through the sense of the tragic to a hope and an assurance which is 'beyond tragedy.' The cross, which stands at the centre of the Christian world-view, reveals both the seriousness of human sin and the purpose and power of God to overcome it. It reveals man violating the will of God in his highest moral and spiritual achievements (in Roman law and Jewish religion) and God absorbing this evil into Himself in the very moment of its most vivid expression. Christianity's view of history is tragic insofar as it recognizes evil as an inevitable concomitant of even the highest spiritual enterprises. It is beyond tragedy inasfar as it does not regard evil as inherent in existence itself but as finally under the dominion of a good God." [32]

Niebuhr here lays great stress on the truth that history and hence the life of man, yes his whole existence, would be entirely emptied of meaning by an eternity which is wholly apart from history and time, as mysticism conceives eternity to be. On the other hand, an eternity which rules over time, guarantees all fulfillment so that history need not itself seek for a fulfillment in and through itself. In his concept of time Niebuhr is actually contending for nothing else than the preservation of relation in tension between God and man. Eternity means actually God in His uniqueness and power, and history means basically the position and existence of man, existence in the special sense of relatedness to other existences, existence in society.

That the relatedness of time and eternity is full of tension, or as Niebuhr puts it, is dialectical—one might question whether *paradoxical* would not be a more accurate term—is proved when in the meeting of eternity and time, centred at the cross, eternity most divests itself of its eternal nature. Eternity stoops to enter time in order to satisfy that hunger for eternity which time vainly sought to appease by an independent fulfillment of its own. Paradoxically it is at the peak of its greatest and most impressive achievements—Roman law and Jewish religion—that time encounters eternity humbling itself for time's sake. And time's inability to find eternal fulfillment in itself is then revealed as it seeks in its pride of achievement to overcome eternity bending down to time, to destroy it in order to free itself from an accusing Other. Thus it pronounces judgment upon itself, for in its victory there is nothing eternal, but only unfulfilled time.

But eternity has demonstrated in time, by its own sacrifice, that it could be eternally and completely satisfied in itself, yet chooses not to be so satisfied and wills to fulfil itself in time. Therefore the nature of time has become wholly different, since it can now have an unrestricted fulfillment in eternity, in this paradoxical-dialectical relationship, and only there.

The question of the relation between time and eternity includes therefore the question of the meaninglessness or meaningfulness of time, and time needs no longer to search after a fulfillment which already lies within time in the cross which judges time and its self-sufficiency. Therefore a denial of the relation of time and eternity, whether in Naturalism or in Mysticism, is always a futile and foolish denial of reality. For this reason, the Christian conception of time and the Christian interpretation of history are always "beyond tragedy."

If in the preceding description of the tense relation of time and eternity and their dramatic encounter at the cross we substitute for "eternity," God in Christ, Lord of time and eternal God-Man; and for "time," finite man with his sinful rejection of God revealing Himself in Christ who "humbled himself"; we find in

Niebuhr's presentation of the relation of time and eternity not only their true significance but also the heart of the whole Christian gospel.

The meaning of the old theological phrase *Christus pro nobis* becomes clear to us, as the expression of what God has done for us in Christ. He has broken into our finiteness from His eternity and sought us out. He has countervailed our sinful departure from Himself, and thereby given a new and transcendent direction to history in time, to human life and to its fulfillment which culminates in the "fulness of time."

We can also understand how the other phrase *Christus in nobis* is connected with the first, since it asserts that in the new uniting of men with God the act at the cross is an act against our sinful self-sufficiency and in behalf of our true life. And further, this Christ is truly God's new creation of our existence here and now; he is new life, *our* new life. Apart from the act of the cross so understood, our own existence can be neither comprehended nor completed nor fulfilled, but must remain unreal. The cross is an act both for us and in us. Christ in us is the new man, living from the new, living bond with God, understanding himself in this bond and by it acting in society. God's activity for and in society comes to pass in the restoration of the individual, operates through the new, living Christian community in society. Christ in us is the creator, bearer, guarantor and fulfiller of life in history, and so its judge and fulfiller at the end of the days.

We can now perceive what Reinhold Niebuhr means by the theological interpretation of history. It is nothing but—he is determined it shall be nothing but—reflection upon the Christ-event as the basis of the understanding of history. We see why the tense relation of time and eternity is so important and can be neither modified nor sacrificed. If it were, the reality of time and eternity as revealed in the depths of religious insight would be lost for the sake of a cheap and unreal consistency in man's rational self-deception; and man, in the desire to preserve his life, would lose his true life, the life of Christ in us, a life founded on the loving relatedness of God and man, which ends all man's attempts to flee from reality.

The "sermonic essays" which follow are all modulations of this one theme and present special applications of it to various specific problems. The first essay, which takes its text from II Cor. 6: 4–10, bears the title "As Deceivers, Yet True." It attempts to explain the incoherence of all theological affirmations, without excusing it as a weakness of theology or praising it as a fine art.

"Time is a succession of events. Yet mere succession is not time. Time has reality only through a meaningful relationship of its successions. Therefore time is real only as it gives successive expressions of principles and powers which lie outside of it. Yet every suggestion of the principle of a process must be expressed in terms of the temporal process, and every idea of the God who is the ground of the world must be expressed in some terms taken from the world. The temporal process is like the painter's flat canvas. It is one dimension upon which two dimensions must be recorded. This can be done only by symbols which deceive for the sake of truth." [33]

"It is therefore true, to account for the meaningfulness of life in terms of the relation of every thing to a creative centre and source of meaning. But the truth . . . can be expressed only in terms which outrage reason." [34]

The incoherence of all theological statements naturally increases the nearer they come to the centre of the Christian message. It is clear that this incoherence both is a part of and offers convincing proof of man's inability, after his relatedness to God has been sinfully broken, to surmount incoherence by reason alone. God's revelation in time in Jesus Christ sharply illuminates this incoherence.

"Yet the revelation of God in the Incarnation is not of itself the redemption. Christianity believes that Christ died to save men from sin. It has a gospel which contains a crucifixion as well as an incarnation, a cross as well as a manger. The doctrine of the atoning death of the Son of God upon the cross has led to many theological errors, among them to theories of substitutionary atonement which outrage the moral sense. There is in fact no theory of the atonement which is quite as satisfying as the simple statements of the vicarious death of Christ in the Gospels. This may mean that faith is able to sense and appropriate an ultimate truth too deep for human reason. This is the foolishness of God which is wiser than the wisdom of men. The modern world has found not only the theories of atonement but the idea of atonement itself absurd. It rebelled not only against theories of a sacrifice which ransomed man from the devil's clutches or of a sacrifice which appeased the anger of a vindictive divine Father; it regarded the very idea of reconciliation between God and man as absurd." [35]

Niebuhr intends to eliminate the usual antitheses of God and world, nature and grace, sin and redemption, in which two entities of more or less equal magnitude are set opposite each other on the same level. He insists strongly that:

"Most profoundly the atonement of Christ is a revelation of what life actually is. It is tragic from the standpoint of human striving." [36]

Such antitheses are then more than dubious. For there is only life and death, being and non-being. Consequently reality appears only on one side of the antithesis. On the other side is nothing but the negation of reality and therefore (strictly construed), also self-negation. Sin as the negation of life's reality, in itself without existence, subsists only because man misappropriates and squanders the life granted to him in the love of God. In his self-will he tears his life free from its bond to God; he turns to the unreal in order to win for himself by a God-like act of creation god-like freedom and a god-like existence. Actually, he forfeits his only possibility of real existence, which is existence in God, his real freedom, and his human power to create. It is not life that is tragic; certainly it is not tragic in itself. The sin of man is tragic, perverting man's will into a self-centred determination to make his decisions about life by his own volition without being in communion with God. True life is to live in God. Every negative in the world has its root in human sin. Man's sin in its turn is negated by God, for only so can the sinner be rescued from tragedy—in the original Greek meaning of the word. The divine "Yes" to the sinner means an inexorable "No" to every temptation of man. It redeems life, the gift of God's love, and retrieves it out of the context where life itself loses its being and becomes non-being.

Knowledge of sin then means to Niebuhr that we are recalled by God's love and hence we ourselves concur in the affirmation of true life against its corruption through sin. Hence also we can recognize the unreality of that which before appeared to us as life's great and terrifying and tragic reality. The cross is the revelation of this tremendous reversal of all values. There the possibility for man to change his life to life-destroying death, by asserting and obstinately maintaining his self-directed life against the true love of God, faces final judgment and is brought to naught. This is actually the negation of a negation upon which the truth of life shines with a fullness of love that reaches even to death, the last and final negation of the human possibility of sinful independence. At the cross and the resurrection the conquest of negation is completed, so that man now in his own living can be restored to the life which is from and in God.

Niebuhr's affirmation of the universality and the full primacy of life from God is an extension of what has been said of eternity and time. He makes an end of the false particularism of the church's message of salvation which gives God too little honor and sin too much, since they are regarded as two equal realities, joining battle on a level. His new insight, however, means that now the totality of all existence is seen facing a wholly new hazard, for there is truly no area in the whole world where final choice between being or non-being can be evaded.

Sin has gained a wholly new and very much more serious significance. It is no longer merely weakness or incompleteness, no longer only a legal misdemeanor with only legal penalties. In the most profound sense of the words it is existential suicide, with all the consequences of suicide for the individual and all associated with him, since it is intentional denial of the reality of the life which God Himself vouchsafed as His loving gift. It is the veritable denial of being and of life itself. Therefore man never conquers sin by some special exertion of his own powers. On the contrary, when man seeks by his own power to establish and justify his position before God, the negative nature of sin becomes much more clear and produces greater negative results in his relations with other men, as his desperate efforts to justify himself involve him in injustice and guilt toward his fellowmen.

This theme occupies Niebuhr in a second essay which considers the history of the tower of Babel, Gen. 11:1–9.

"The pretensions of human cultures and civilisations are the natural consequence of a profound and ineradicable difficulty in all human spirituality. Man is mortal. That is his fate. Man pretends not to be mortal. That is his sin. Man is a creature of time and place, whose perspectives and insights are invariably conditioned by his immediate circumstances. But man is not merely the prisoner of time and place. He touches the fringes of the eternal. He is not content to be merely American man, or Chinese man, or bourgeois man, or man of the twentieth century. He wants to be man. He is not content with his truth. He seeks *the* truth. His memory spans the ages in order that he may transcend his age. His restless mind seeks to comprehend the meaning of all cultures so that he may not be caught within the limitations of his own.

"Thus man builds towers of the spirit from which he may survey larger horizons than those of his class, race and nation. This is a necessary human enterprise. . . . But it is also inevitable that these towers should be towers of Babel, that they should pretend to reach higher than their real height; and should claim a finality which they cannot possess. The truth man finds and speaks is, for all of his efforts to transcend himself, still his truth. The 'good' which he discovers, is for all of his efforts to disassociate from his own interest and interests, still his 'good.' The higher the tower is built to escape unnecessary limitations of the human imagination, the more certain it will be to defy necessary and inevitable limitations. Thus sin corrupts the highest as well as the lowest achievements of human life. Human pride is greatest when it is based upon solid achievements; but the achievements are never great enough to justify its pretensions. This pride is at least one aspect of what Christian orthodoxy means by 'original sin.' It is not so much an inherited corruption as an inevitable taint upon the spirituality of a finite creature, always enslaved to time and place, never completely enslaved and always under the illusion that the measure of his emancipation is greater than it really is." [37]

Niebuhr rightly warns us to consider carefully the nature of man lest we fall into a misconception of human reality. A continual urge to break through his own finitude belongs to the essence of man. Niebuhr is far from labeling this urge sin, for it is in itself a sign that man cannot be content in himself. It is therefore a sign of man's need of the eternal God if his finitude and his mortality are not to become the torturing denial of his whole existence. The Augustinian "Cor nostrum inquietum est donec requiescat in te, Domine" would be the destined end of man's inevitable unrest.

But here the ultimately inexplicable Mystery of sin enters—man is not willing to receive from the hand of God the grace of immortality which is wholly inseparable from God, and only possible in loving communion with Him. Man claims immortality for himself and seeks it by attempting to transcend himself. This attempt results in a self-exaggeration which cannot alter the nature of the self, for subject and object are the same. Man gains only malformation and the loss of the real self.

Niebuhr's careful distinction between sin and the God-created nature of man is fundamental. Niebuhr, as we shall see later, has taken warning from the history of theology. Precisely *ad majorem gloriam dei*, one dare not confuse the work of God's creation with human sin. If the words of the elder Blumhardt, "God is not a wrecker, but a builder" were better understood and more heeded, perhaps men would not so ardently build the towers of Babel. We must ask ourselves whether sin is not more fundamental and burdensome, whether the guilt of man is not greater, because sin does not have its origin as a deterministic necessity in the very nature of man. We have every reason to listen carefully to the history of the tower of Babel.

"The Tower of Babel myth is one of the first, as it is one of the most vivid, expressions of the quality of biblical religion. The characteristic distinction of biblical religion, in contrast to culture religions, is that the latter seek to achieve the eternal and divine by some discipline of the mind or heart, whether mystical or rational, while the former believes that a gulf remains fixed between the Creator and the creature which even revelation does not completely bridge. Every revelation of the divine is relativised by the finite mind which comprehends it. Consequently God, though revealed, remains veiled; his thoughts are not our thoughts nor his ways our ways. As high as the heaven is above the earth so high are his thoughts beyond our thoughts and his ways beyond our ways. The worship of such a God leads to contrition; not merely to a contrite recognition of the conscious sins of pride and arrogance which the human spirit commits, but to a sense of guilt for the inevitable and inescapable pride involved in every human enterprise, even in the highest and most perfect or, more correctly, particularly in the highest and noblest human enterprise." [38]

Niebuhr's serious concern lies precisely where neither those who view sin deterministically nor those who view it optimistically can penetrate. For the first group think that nothing can be done; and the others believe that, since ultimately everything will work out properly, nothing needs to be done. But Niebuhr is most earnestly striving to persuade man in his total but voluntary sinfulness to lay hold on the whole grace of God which will compel him to work eagerly—not to redeem the world, because that has been done by God and will be done by Him, but to undertake in gratitude to God man's real task in the world. This is true life.

It follows naturally that Niebuhr finds new meaning in the church. Not that he came by chance to consider the problem of the church and found it crucial. The problem arose necessarily in the course of his thinking, so that if we make the effort we can find for ourselves his angle of approach.

"The church is that place in human society where men are disturbed by the word of the eternal God, which stands as a judgment upon human aspirations. But it is also the place where the word of mercy, reconciliation and consolation is heard: 'Thou dost well that it was in thine heart.' Here human incompleteness is transcended though not abolished. Here human sin is overcome by the divine mercy, though man remains a sinner. No church can lift man out of the partial and finite history in which all human life stands. Every interpretation of the church which promises an 'efficient grace,' by which man ceases to be man and enters prematurely into the Kingdom of God, is a snare and a delusion. The church is not the kingdom of God. The church is the place in human society where the Kingdom of God impinges upon all human enterprises through the divine word, and where the grace of God is made available to those who have accepted His judgment." [39]

The primary office of the church for Niebuhr is the preaching of judgment and grace. The church is never itself the mediator of restoration; it is the place where the word of God like a two-edged sword divides truly between sinner and sin, a division which man himself, even in the church, can never make.

"The sin of man arises from his effort to establish his own security; and the sin of the false prophet lies in the effort to include this false security within the ultimate security of faith. The false security to which all men are tempted is the security of power. The primary insecurity of human life arises from its weakness and finiteness. Man is a frail little insect buffeted by forces vaster than he. Man is a defenseless creature, the prey of armed and brutal men. What is more natural than that he should seek to transmute his weakness into strength? That he should desire enough power to hold the enmity of nature at bay and to intimidate his human foes? So natural is this that we will concede its necessity and refrain from challenging it by pacifistic moralizing." [40]

But: "All power leads to pride and injustice; to the pride of 'them that despise me,' the pride of men who have forgotten that they are creatures and that no creaturely human strength is strong enough to make nature purely the servant of man rather than his nemesis; to the injustice of those who create their security at the expense of the security and freedom of others. The sin of pride, to which the prophets of Israel were so sensitive, is more obvious in our day than in theirs. Yet there are fewer prophets to recognise and challenge it." [41]

Niebuhr sees an unbroken line leading from the pride which is rooted in power, crossing the false security which man gains from his pride, to a superficial morality.

"Yet this moralism is false prophecy. Its error can be most briefly described as its failure to understand what Christian theology has meant by original sin. It does not see that man is not free to extricate himself from the vicious circle of sin, even if he recognizes it as a vicious circle." [42]

Here we see how determined Niebuhr is, because he is so exceedingly sensitive to the evidences of sin in society, not to minimize the disturbed relations in society by any assumptions about the goodness of men. He is bent on searching out the deepest source of the corruption of society, the source in man himself, since from man's corruption flow all the injustices of society. He has therefore never been able to speak of sin lightly as a weakness or an incompleteness. He sees the existence of man under that doom which the Greeks expressed in their tragedies. This is then the place to contrast Christianity and Greek tragedy.

"Christianity and Greek tragedy agree that guilt and creativity are inextricably interwoven. But Christianity does not regard the inevitability of guilt in all human creativity as inherent in the nature of human life. Sin emerges, indeed, out of freedom and is possible only because man is free; but it is done in freedom, and therefore man and not life bears responsibility for it. It does indeed accompany every creative act; but the evil is not a part of the creativity. It is the consequence of man's self-centredness and egotism by which he destroys the harmony of existence. The fact that he does this is not an occasion for admiration but for pity: 'Weep for yourselves' remains Christianity's admonition to all who involve themselves in sin and guilt, whether by unconscious submission to forces greater than their will or by consciously affirming these forces." [43]

In him who overcame sin on the cross, the difference becomes plain. Jesus Christ dies not as a tragic hero but as the revealer of life.

"The Saviour . . . dies upon the cross. He dies not because he has sinned but because he has not sinned. He proves thereby that sin is so much a part of existence that sinlessness cannot maintain itself in it. But he also proves that sin is not a necessary and inherent characteristic of life. Evil is not a part of God, nor yet a part of essential man. This Saviour is a revelation of the goodness of God and the essential goodness of man, *i.e.*, the second Adam. He is indeed defeated in history but in that very defeat proves that he cannot be ultimately defeated. That is, he reveals that it is God's nature to swallow up evil in Himself and destroy it. Life in its deepest essence is not only good but capable of destroying the evil which has been produced in it. Life is thus not at war with itself. Its energy is not in conflict with its order. Hence the Saviour truly says: 'Weep not for me.' Christianity stands beyond tragedy. If there are tears for this man on the cross they cannot be tears of 'pity and terror.' The cross does not reveal life at cross purposes with itself. On the contrary, it declares that what seems to be an inherent defect in life itself is really a contingent defect in the soul of each man, the defect of the sin which he commits in his freedom. If he can realize that fact, if he can weep for himself, if he can repent, he can also be saved. . . . His hope and faith will separate the character of life in its essential reality from life as it is revealed in sinful history." [44]

In all this discussion, Niebuhr is seeking to solve the problem christocentrically, that is, strictly speaking, in Jesus Christ crucified. He views life always as life from God, given by God; however much he may also be concerned with actual human existence. The central problem for him lies in the fact that he can never regard as sinful this life which is God's loving gift to man and through man to society. Such life is both the original state of man and the new position to which man can come from his present broken relatedness—a new and harmonious union with God and society. Yet this new position is not a possibility which man can attain for himself, since all man's attainable possibilities are inevitably doomed to misuse in his attempts at self-rescue.

Niebuhr affirms both the absolute goodness of life and the radical involvement of man in sin—although the latter is not to be understood as an explanatory theory of total depravity. Only through the absolute goodness of God-given life is sin really recognised by man as sin. And only when the negation of sin is known, can life be recognised as true new life.

From this position, and only from this position, Niebuhr can see sin in the world as the destructive factor in the relationships of the world, for only from this position can it be seen rightly. From this position, all optimistic liberal illusions reveal themselves as actually errors and deceptions; and therefore as doubly dangerous because they obscure the true nature of sin. From this position, all man's hopes of building the kingdom of God on earth by his own powers become impossible.

Consequently Niebuhr feels it fundamentally important to clear away the mistaken hopes and deceptions of men so that a clear view may make the true solution possible. We shall now review briefly his rejection of false possibilities that we may see the depth and breadth of his understanding of the nature of sin.

In so doing we shall also discover that Niebuhr finds here a new and determinative approach for his interpretation of history. For as truly as God revealed in Jesus Christ on the cross what true life is and always shall be, so true is it that the fulfillment of time, the removal of the tension in the relation between God, man and society is a possibility only of the undisputed will of God. His rule ends human self-will—that is, ends sin. Thus neither the action of individual men nor human history as a whole can fulfil itself. The efforts of man to achieve self-fulfillment always negate the fulfillment of history by God.

"We live in a world in which the Kingdom is not established, in which the fate of the King of love is crucifixion. In large areas of life our concern must therefore be to prevent life from destroying life." [45]

We may perhaps be reminded here of the central idea in the philosophy of Albert Schweitzer and of what he has said of reverence for life. But only a hasty comparison is needed to show that Niebuhr has founded his judgment on a basis more evangelical and closer to the Reformation than Schweitzer's, one which allows him to reach more sharply defined and more valid conclusions. Niebuhr differs essentially from Schweitzer because for Niebuhr the act which preserves true life is the act of Christ, or as he calls it here "the work of the second Adam." Only through Christ in us can true life be ours, never through our own work of which we could boast before God; for:

"the second Adam is not a simple moral possibility for a sinful human nature, as the liberal church has believed. The second Adam is crucified by the first Adam who is trying to be good and is seeking to build up governments and churches and standards of conduct which will hold sin in check. Jesus is destroyed by the chief priests and elders, the princes of the world; and his chief opponents are the best people of his day, the Pharisees." [46]

There are then two sides to Niebuhr's picture of history: on God's side, history is determined by the concept of life; but on man's side, it is stamped with the concept of sin. Life, as God's loving act, is God's imprint upon creation. In creation God, by the gift of life forever inseparable from Him, first made possible the historical existence in time of all creatures, among them man in his own salient position. In spite of man's sinful turning away from his Creator and so destroying the true relatedness between God, man and society, man could never entirely break life's bond to God. A complete severance would have resulted in the immediate advent of death and the complete annihilation of life.

But man, conscious of his peculiar station between heaven and earth, has felt driven, in ever more violent protest against his finitude, into absurd rebellion and fantastic denial which become ever more destructive of the relation between man and society. That man's rebellion is rebellion against God was proved most clearly when God in His Son Jesus Christ, the true Life, revealed Himself on earth as love. And sin as man's rejection of his function in a society truly related to God showed itself most plainly in the involvement of his highest achievements in the crucifixion of the Son of God. Final judgment on man's achievements was pronounced when the only-begotten Son of God, in His death on Golgotha, took upon Himself fully, once for all, man's total rebellion against God with its consequence which is death, the annihilation of life.

This means the triumph of life over death so that now, although the history of human sin stands always under its accompanying judgment as rebellion and destruction of relatedness, yet at the end of history there is revealed life in God. And this life wholly negates man's denial of life from God, and is the fulfillment of the true meaning of life in history.

Niebuhr's interpretation of history can then be roughly represented by two lines, one proceeding from God's eternity as the line of life through and in history until it meets and is crossed by the other line—the line of sinful rebellion against God which runs upward from before the beginnings of known history to the high peak of rebellion in the crucifixion of the Son of God, thence to drop towards the judgment at the end of the days. These lines which, to the eye of man blinded by his rebellion, are hidden as the foolishness of God so contrary to man's own wisdom actually cross at the crucifixion of Jesus Christ. From there God's line of life as judgment and fulfillment dominates history. It makes ever more plain the corruption of human sin and the death line extending from it, until at the end of history it shall finally demonstrate that the life of the world, and with it the possibility of human existence is possible only with God. Man's assertion of independence and his concomitant rejection of his bond to God shall appear for what they are, the actual denial of reality.

Sin then involves two impossibilities. Its existence of itself is impossible, since it can exist only in the God-given possibility of human freedom. And it is equally impossible for sin to attain its goal of complete rejection of God. At the end of the days, sin will be exposed as the great impossibility which deceitfully played its part as man's possibility. And life from God and in God, the new, great possibility of the second Adam, of man in Christ, will stand revealed as fullness of life. Throughout history, this real possibility has stood above man, always denying as impossible every possibility attainable by man's own powers, judging it as rebellion and condemning all man's desperate attempts to realize himself in sinful separation from God.

From this interpretation of history as the history of God's action in all histories in man's sense, Niebuhr's sharp criticism of prevalent contemporary theologies is understandable. These theologies have been unwilling to admit the seriousness of sin either as a fundamental rebellion against God or as man's full responsibility. They have also not recognised the authority, the dominance and the absolute nature of the action of God in history. Therefore Niebuhr emphasizes again and again, more and more sharply, the lines of his own thought concerning sin in its theological significance and especially in its significance for the relation of man to society.

From this new conception of sin is gained a wholly new understanding of the eschatological statements in the Bible and the Apostles' Creed. They have acquired a new and definitive meaning after the long period in which they were taken as meaningless and outworn fantasies by theologians unwilling to recognise the seriousness of sin. This attitude has been especially common in America as the rejection by various denominations of eschatology as the theme for the ecumenical conference at Evanston showed.

"It makes a difference whether men are good or evil and whether they do good or evil. In spite of all moral relativism we know fairly well what good and evil are." [47]

"Yet there is this other side of the gospel teaching and of all biblical thought: It makes no difference whether men are good or evil in the sight of God, because they are all in need of God's mercy. It makes no difference whether they have laboured long or briefly in the vineyard, the first is as much in need of divine grace as the last. It is because the first are so greatly tempted to forget this that they frequently become last and the last first." [48]

This brings Niebuhr to the differentiation between positive and unconscious sin. But he can see here only a difference of intensity and form, not a fundamental distinction.

"The unconscious sins, of which all men are guilty, are sometimes interpreted in purely negative terms. They are supposed to represent the inertia of nature operating against the moral ambitions of the spirit. Yet there are, strictly speaking, no purely negative sins. The natural impulse, which is subtly compounded with devotion to ideals in human behavior, is never purely natural; that is, it is not merely the animal in man, contending against the distinctively human. The freedom of the human spirit reaches down into the furthest depths of nature and disturbs its natural tranquillity, endowing natural passions with a potency unknown in the animal world. . . .

"The positive sins of the spirit are Promethean. The spirit of man proudly o'erleaps its moral infirmities and claims an unlawful divinity. The negative sins of man are Dionysian. In them the spirit sharpens all the dark unconscious impulses of nature and sets them at war with the requirements of virtue. Therefore what seems to be negative is not purely negative. When we leave undone the things we ought to have done we are busy doing those things which we ought not to have done. We are prevented from virtue by slavery to passions which exert a more cruel mastery than the inertia of nature." [49]

There is a two-fold meaning in the expression "in the world but not of the world," and man must always see his life in this two-fold aspect.

"The world is . . . alienated from its true character. Men do not know their true relation to God. Therefore they make themselves God and their minds are darkened by the confusion caused by this self-glorification. The kingdom of truth is consequently not the kingdom of some other world. It is the picture of what this world ought to be. This kingdom is thus not of this world, inasfar as the world is constantly denying the fundamental laws of human existence. Yet it is of this world. It is not some realm of eternal perfection which has nothing to do with historical existence. It constantly impinges upon man's every decision and is involved in every action." [50]

The discontinuity of Niebuhr's dialectical statements witnesses that he is really striving to bring God's truth into relation to man as man now lives in his sinful and therefore fragmentary existence. The whole abyss of sin is disclosed before him. It shows clearly in its absolute blackness against the bright background of the truth that God has neither willed it nor assented to it, but has reversed it by His saving act through Christ, and will at the end of the days end all its confusion. Sin in itself is not an essential ingredient of the God-given nature of man, and this means that man by God's act will be brought to the fulfillment of his own reality which is now hidden in the darkness of sin.

So Niebuhr's dialectic from beginning to end is a dialectic required by our finitude in time. Its necessity is grounded in the nature of sin which makes it impossible to speak truth about the reality of God and the situation of man in his sinfulness except in dialectical discontinuity. But since sin possesses no reality in itself and exists only from the voluntary breaking of relatedness by man and man's denial of God, the discontinuous dialectical statements do not have an absolute validity.

Important as is the whole concept of life begun from God before the beginning of history for the understanding of history, equally important in Niebuhr's thought is the end of history as the fulfillment of life through God. History first acquires meaning from this end. His essays reach a fitting conclusion with the consideration of the fullness of time as affirmed in the final words of the Creed: "I believe in the forgiveness of sin, the resurrection of the body and the life everlasting."

"Soul and body are one. Man is in nature. He is, for that reason, not of nature. It is important to emphasize both points. Man is the creature of necessity and the child of freedom. His life is determined by natural contingencies; yet his character develops by rising above nature's necessities and accidents. With reference to the purposes of his life, it is significant that the necessities of nature are accidents and contingencies. Sometimes he is able to bend nature's necessities to his own will; sometimes he must submit his destiny to them. But whether he dominates or submits to nature, he is never merely an element in nature. The simple proof is that his life is not wholly determined but is partly self-determining. This is a very obvious fact of experience which is easily obscured by philosophies, which either lift man wholly out of nature or make him completely identical with it, usually for no better reason than to fit him into a completely consistent scheme of analysis." [51]

Because the unity of body and soul in man is a fact, sin cannot be relegated to one part of man only. It inheres in all decision and action where the whole personality is bound together, in the spirit. (This point we shall later investigate more carefully and offer a somewhat less one-sided judgment.)

"The root of sin is in spirit and not in nature. The assertion of that fact distinguishes Christianity both from naturalism, which denies the reality of sin, and from various types of mysticism and dualism, which think that finiteness as such, or in other words the body, is the basis of evil. Even when sin is not selfishness but sensuality, man's devotion to his physical life and to sense enjoyments differs completely from animal normality. It is precisely because he is free to centre his life in certain physical processes and to lift them out of the harmonious relationships in which nature has them, that man falls into sin. . . . Whatever the relation of sensuality and selfishness in the realm of human evil, whether they are two types of sin or whether one is derived from the other, it is obvious that both are the fruits of the spirit and not of the flesh." [52]

The fullness of life for man in unity of body, soul, and spirit, must therefore mean the removal of the possibility of the chaos due to man's sinful, self-willed separation of himself from all true relatedness. The essential for all possibility of relatedness is unquestioning communion with God. In such communion, the temptation no longer arises to build upon a new centre of *self*-relatedness which destroys the whole.

"The possibilities of the fulfilment of this life transcend our experience not because the soul is immortal and the body is mortal but because this human life, soul and body, is both immersed in flux and above it, and because it involves itself in sin in this unique position from which there is no escape by its own powers. The fulfilment of life beyond the possibilities of this existence is a justified hope, because of our human situation, that is, because a life which knows the flux in which it stands cannot be completely a part of that flux. On the other hand this hope is not one which fulfils itself by man's own powers. God must complete what remains incomplete in human existence. This is true both because there is no simple division in human life between what is mortal and what is immortal so that the latter could slough off the former; and because the incompleteness of human life is not only finiteness but sin." [53]

It is important and noteworthy that now when Niebuhr is considering the fulfillment of life in the fulfillment of history, he finds such fulfillment possible only as the fulfillment of community among men, in the final solution of "the social question." It is the love of God, creating community, which creates the new man and sets him in the rightly ordered relatedness to God and society. Therefore the love which transforms us cannot be limited to ourselves and cut off from our fellowmen. So cut off, it would atrophy. This love must build true and genuine community in which the life of the individual can be fulfilled in the mutual life without becoming lost by absorption into the mass.

The close of the Apostles' Creed witnesses to this fulfillment, the promise of God.

"It is significant that there is no religion, or for that matter no philosophy of life, whether explicit or implicit, which does not hold out the hope of the fulfilment of life in some form or other. Since it is man's nature to be emancipated of the tyranny of the immediate present and to transcend the processes of nature in which he is involved, he cannot exist without having his eyes upon the future. The future is the symbol of his freedom.

"The Christian view of the future is complicated by the realization of the fact that the very freedom which brings the future into view has been the occasion for the corruption of the present in the heart of man. Mere development of what he now is cannot save man, for the development will heighten all the contradictions in which he stands. Nor will emancipation from the law of development and the march of time through entrance into a timeless and motionless eternity save him. That could only annihilate him. His hope consequently lies in a forgiveness which will overcome not his finiteness but his sin, and a divine omnipotence which will complete his life without destroying its essential nature. Hence the final expression of hope in the Apostolic Creed: 'I believe in the forgiveness of sins, the resurrection of the body and the life everlasting' is a much more sophisticated expression of hope in ultimate fulfilment than all its modern substitutes. It grows out of a realization of the total human situation which the modern mind has not fathomed. The symbols by which this hope is expressed are, to be sure, difficult. The modern mind imagines that it has rejected the hope because of this difficulty. But the real cause of the rejection lies in its failure to understand the problem of human existence in all its complexity." [54]

We have followed Reinhold Niebuhr through the various essays in *Beyond Tragedy*. This is the last of his books to show primarily the origin and the progressive development of his conception of sin. Since our purpose is to demonstrate that the doctrine of sin is the determinative structural element in his theology, it was especially necessary to investigate it in relation to that theology from two angles: how his thought as a whole and his point of view influenced the formation of his conception of sin, and how, on the other hand, this conception of sin influenced the further development of his theology as a whole. To do this, we must first understand Niebuhr's doctrine of sin in relation to his whole position and then come back to the concept of sin.

We have tried to make clear that the fundamental position of Niebuhr was determined by his early experiences as a young pastor in Detroit. There the problem had already expanded for him into the complete arch of the bridge of relatedness between God, religion, man and society. It then became clear that this relatedness was grievously broken, and Niebuhr set himself to investigate the separate points of stress in the ruined structure. From this investigation came the discovery that all the breaks were in fact caused by one central derangement, at the centre of the life of man. From this centre, destructive forces radiate to the whole relationship of men to God and to society, and in ever greater waves widen and deepen the breaks in human unity.

The bonds to God and to society are not of equal weight, for the relation between God and man is basic. Man's whole possibility of life exists only through relatedness to God as God Himself ordered it.

God turns lovingly to man and gives him life, and this life has true reality only in harmonious communion with God. The repudiation of this communion by man results in the fundamental perversion of his existence. Man involves religion in this perversion so far as its institutional manifestations are subject to him, so that religion becomes separated from the source which alone can sustain it. It is the life-creating and life-preserving communion between God and man which gives man his unique superiority over the rest of the creatures, the freedom of his self-consciousness. The destruction of this relatedness drives him in the resulting insecurity to attempt to win security for himself. He seeks to raise himself above the limits and the finitude of his existence. But this means that all the possibilities and powers which are given him by God for the purpose of relatedness with God and with his fellowmen in society, he exerts for his own aggrandizement and for the repudiation of God and society.

So man actually gains an intensification of his existent energy which he employs for mastering all existences opposed to him. Here is the origin of injustice as the cultural, social and economic effect of sinful self-centredness. The culmination in the rival political powers of today shows most clearly that man is engaged in the desperate attempt to establish himself by his own might against all else. Here the catastrophic effects of such efforts are most clearly manifest. Man in the attempt to save himself summons the very forces which with the same motive press upon him and seek to destroy him. He precipitates his own ruin by his attempt to prevent it or at the least to escape it.

But Niebuhr is not satisfied with any formulation of a conception of sin which might be a part of anthropological phenomenology, or even leave room for various hypotheses on the true origin and essential nature of sin. Neither the whole unfathomable depth nor the full meaning of sin would then be recognised. Also it would still be allowable to talk of the conquest of sin. Therefore Niebuhr asserts that no anthropological phenomenology can deal with sin.

The whole truth of man's sinful rebellion, corrupting and destroying human existence, can be known only through God's revelation. Immanent interpretations of life and of history, which declare that man can no longer know himself in his true position only because he has accidentally slipped out of his true relation, miss what gives definitive meaning and direction. Such interpretations are themselves a part of human error and corruption, and the error grows continually greater since they assume the corrupted and unrelated existence of man as basic, and promise immanent solutions which must all prove illusory. Since they thus increase man's blindness, they drive him the more certainly to catastrophe.

These interpretations also lack a clear view of the present because they cannot penetrate to the past from which the valid hereafter is first made known. Creation and eschatology are alike ignored. Immanent interpretations of life and history remain meaningless because they do not proceed from true life but from the perversion of life by man. They cannot know life's true fulfillment but can offer only a vain hope for an impossible self-regulation and correction of life's confusion through men.

The truth about life, the real basis of human existence, can be revealed only by the Giver of this life, by God. By God's revelation the derangement of man separated from his relatedness with God is sharply illuminated at the moment of its climax, when man at the peak of his own self-assertion killed God's life-bringer, Jesus Christ, on Golgotha. There the rejection of life and the destruction of life by isolating it from its origin in God is fully revealed; and there also the rejection was overcome by God when He Himself in His Son paid the price of death for man and man's rebellion. Then it was revealed that life itself can be annulled no more than can God Himself; that all human life lives by life from God, even when—rather, especially when—this dependence is most entirely and most vehemently denied. God, bending in love to the sinner, presents the strongest negation of the lovelessness of man's attempt at self-assertion.

Life is therefore never something existing in and for itself. Its essence, its vivifying force is love. Thus God, uniting in Himself life and love, was moved to send His inexhaustible life streaming forth, turning lovingly to men even—or rather especially—when men least deserve it. So also human life cannot find its true destiny in the attempt to gain self-satisfaction and self-certainty, for these demand separateness, the breaking of the bond to the Giver of life, and makes impossible life's fulfillment in society.

The prophets of religion with their recognition of this fundamental truth of life have again and again through the centuries raised their voices in judgment and warning against the threat to life by sin. They have pointed to the fulfillment of life in the final judgment and the eradication of the rebellion of man in history, and they have made it clear that history becomes meaningful through the judging and redeeming act of God. The truth about history, like the truth about life, is closely bound to history itself, but it also transcends history. It corresponds to the life of man, confused by sin, in which man's knowledge and thinking, his reasoning power, partake of the fragmentation of his life so that he can neither grasp nor express the reality and truth of life without distortion and fragmentation.

The whole truth will always reach man from the Beyond, in the words of myth, because man himself is always trying to credit the untruths of his own sinful assumptions as the presupposed criteria of truth. It is necessary not only to recognize the necessity of myth, but also to understand what it means to take the word of myth with absolute seriousness. To take myth seriously means to take seriously what myth intends to be and to create—the new acceptance of the relatedness of God and man. When man understands that the essence of myth is God's loving claim upon him, he does not resent the fact that, because of human fragmentation, supra-rational and supra-historical truth must be clothed in a unique and transcendant form in order to win rational and historical comprehension. That comprehension dare not judge and scorn myth; it must let itself be judged by myth and must treasure it.

Myth is not in itself truth, but in myth the living God reveals Himself as the source of truth in order to bind man again personally to Himself. Myth is not about something, but about somebody—about God who accepts man anew in love.

We have brought together briefly, in broad outline, the result of our investigation. From the final observations it is clear that neither knowledge nor truth can have an abstract significance grounded in itself and self-validating. They serve only to reveal the position of man as dependent upon God, and man's true relation to society as dependent upon and conditioned by his dependence upon God.

The first effort of the young Niebuhr was to bring gospel and world into mutual relation. This has remained the compelling motive for his whole work and has determined the course of his thinking. This thinking could never be purely—although it is predominantly—theological; but dealt with politics, economics, and culture; without, however, becoming entangled in them. Niebuhr's words are always in the world; not of the world, but a vital overture towards it.

When we now turn in the following sections to the two of Reinhold Niebuhr's longer works which contain a more systematic integration and presentation of the ideas in his earlier work, we shall certainly not expect something wholly new, but rather the clarification of what we have already learned. We should remind ourselves that our especial task is to investigate the doctrine of sin as the structural element in his theology. We can therefore in what follows limit ourselves to a demonstration of how strongly this concept of sin dominates Niebuhr's systematic synthesis.

V. Faith and Society as the Poles of the Original and True State of Man

Disorder and Restoration in Nature and History

We must now ask what light Niebuhr's understanding of sin throws on his theology as a whole. All the facets of thought so far presented can now be fitted into a synthesis which will permit a more systematic survey than was possible in our earlier investigation of his thinking.

We shall therefore deal with the two works which more than any others make the attempt to develop his convictions in systematic fashion. Even here dogmatic structure in a strict sense is not attainable for two reasons. The inner and more important is the fact that Niebuhr is never concerned about pure and correct doctrine for its own sake but only about a doctrine in which the reality of man's life in his relatedness to God and man is revealed. Such revelation can of course be only approximate, for no rational wisdom and doctrine can state adequately and correctly the inclusive personal relatedness of man to God and society.

The second reason follows upon that impossibility. Niebuhr is neither by nature nor by profession a systematic theologian; he is a teacher of applied Christianity, and he has understood the whole teaching office for the church and for himself as having no other aim than to bring into mutual relation gospel and world. He has considered himself primarily as a missionary preaching to the world, and as such he has won his influence among non-theologians. The doctrines of the church have served him as tools in the continuing debate between the preacher of the gospel and the modern man who is seeking to understand himself and his world. Should the church ever abandon this aim or no longer know how to help the man of today to understand his true nature and his real destiny, in the midst of his manifold problems, or should modern society definitely and finally refuse to accept correction from the Word of God, then Niebuhr fears for church and society a total collapse into a complete misunderstanding of their own nature and an irrational perversion of the purpose of their existence.

That is the theme of the Gifford lectures which Niebuhr gave in Edinburgh in 1939–40 and later published under the title *The Nature and Destiny of Man.*[1] This is also the basis of the book which appeared in 1949, *Faith and History*[2] in which Niebuhr deals especially with the false interpretation of history in the era of evolutionary thinking, in order to displace it and its errors by Christian Faith. The errors of this evolutionary interpretation of history are not accidental blunders. A picture of man is presented which falsifies his God-given nature and destiny within human society and constitutes rebellion against his true station. It is consequently useless for living.

Niebuhr knows both that man inevitably questions himself and that such questioning is always indecisive and unrewarding. That knowledge is his starting point.

"Man has always been his own most vexing problem. How shall he think of himself? Every affirmation which he may make about his stature, virtue or place in the cosmos becomes involved in contradictions when fully analysed."[3]

Niebuhr begins by taking seriously the age-old questioning of man about himself. He does not desire to impose upon man a strange doctrine, or any doctrine which cannot be incorporated into his experience. This attitude is definite and basic. But he does desire to help man towards a true self-knowledge. Therefore he decisively repudiates all doctrinaire theological and philosophical anthropology. Significantly, he comes close to that formulation of the question which gave rise to modern Existentialism.

But Niebuhr's great service is that, although he frames the question as do the Existentialists, in complete opposition to them he does not seek either the reason for the question or the answer to it in man himself. His question does not run "what is man?" but "what is the original state of man and therefore his true state?". Man's confusion exists not because man cannot come to himself until he achieves a genuine order; but because man, misunderstanding and rejecting his original state, is bent on realizing himself (as Sartre puts it) without any authority which defines him.

To this repudiation of authority beyond man, Niebuhr strongly objects. Man, by such an attempt to realize himself not only misapprehends and distorts his true position, to determine which is the basic problem of contemporary man; he also rejects his own life and makes his own existence untenable. This is what Niebuhr understands as the sin in human disorder. We see then that Niebuhr is using the approach which, since Kierkegaard, has been so prevalent and often so misleading in philosophy. But the solution he seeks will be wholly different.

The reading of the two books just mentioned forces the recognition that Niebuhr's formulation of the problem so closely resembles that of Kierkegaard in *The Sickness unto Death* [4] that one can correctly speak of a Kierkegaardian anthropology. Niebuhr, however, never refers to the relationship although he often quotes the book. It is not easy to decide whether Niebuhr, who certainly was impressed by Kierkegaard,[5] really took from him the formulation of the problem or whether we have here merely a coincidence, although a very significant one.

If Kierkegaard's *The Sickness unto Death* could stand as godfather to the formulation of man's problem in Niebuhr's books, it is equally clear that Emil Brunner's *Der Mensch in Widerspruch* [6] (English translation, *Man in Revolt*) influenced greatly both the question and the direction of Niebuhr's answer, although this connection also was never expressly stated by Niebuhr.

Both connections, however are important for us. We can see how Niebuhr, as the exponent of American theology and its especial bias, altered and shaped his own thinking through continuous, truly ecumenical discussion with the theology of the continent, especially the dialectical theology and its forerunner, Sören Kierkegaard. It is therefore not surprising to find him, as an American, occupied with the same questions which engage the dialectical theology of the continent and the philosophical existentialism which is its contemporary and its opponent.

We shall later consider specifically how great a contribution Niebuhr makes to the further development of both American and European theology just because in spite of all similarities to others he presents a way of thinking which is peculiarly his own. It is enough now to recognize the connection with continental thought as we proceed to the understanding of his conception of man. Niebuhr sees man first and always in his relatedness to God and his fellowmen. Faith and society are for him the poles of man's original state as created by God; poles also therefore of his disintegration and of his true re-integration in nature and history.

We have already said that Niebuhr's interest is explicitly centred on man. The statement is true, but we must immediately add that it does not mean that his view of the world is man-centred. Actually the first statement excludes the second. Whoever takes man seriously must see that man's problem is precisely that he has lost the sense of his destined goal and with it true insight into his own nature. Niebuhr finds here the source of the error in all human self-understanding. It is at this point that words must be spoken which will enable man again to know himself and his true destiny that he may accept that destiny as the reason for his own existence. Such and such only is Niebuhr's purpose in what follows.

He is not so much a theologian as a Christian anthropologist, and he is that not as an abstract, neutral investigator but as a Christian preacher. His desire is that man may learn from the Bible, that from the Bible he may both accept his original state and admit his own guilt as cause for the present disorder; and, still more important, that he may accept redemptive re-ordering in nature and history. So only will man again come to himself as a creature of God directed toward his fellow creatures in love and service.

Certainly if the order "in the beginning" and the re-ordering "at the end of the days" are meant, the frame of nature and history is transcended. But this transcendence points to the deepest secret of man's self-knowledge. Man can understand himself, find and satisfy himself, in nature and history only if understanding comes to him from Beyond nature and history, from God's incursion to him—that is, in his relatedness to God. Therefore every immanent interpretation of man is found to be basically inadequate and unsuited to the real nature of man and so is ultimately rejected.

1. *The Original State of Man*

It may at first seem strange that an "original state" of man should be a subject for discussion. But Niebuhr does not take man from his *hic et nunc* without pre-suppositions, or like Sartre think of him only as moving from his present state toward that which he will become. There is for Niebuhr an *a priori* which basically defines both man's present existence and his future, an indispensible presumption without which man can neither understand himself nor truly be himself. For Niebuhr, man does not set himself in his place, he has been placed. Man cannot succeed in ordering his life unless he first knows and accepts the ordered position previously given him. To that position, which is determined by the turning of God to man and continually leading and accompanying him, man can relate himself and it then becomes possible for him to direct and correct himself.

The Christian delineation of man does not begin with assertions by man; it begins with assertions about man by God. Man's beginning lies in the creative act of God. The essential truth about man in this context is that he was created in the image of God. Therefore man neither originated from himself; nor is his end in himself. He came into existence by the voluntary creative act of a Creator and he is preserved in inner dependence upon his Creator. Man's knowledge of himself and of the world begins here; for here alone, from beyond himself and the world, is man understood in his true nature. Man therefore can never confine himself to only one of two areas; he can neither be satisfied in the narrowness of self-isolation, nor find himself rightly and preserve himself in the wide world.

The uniqueness of man in the whole creation can only be understood from God's revelation.

"God as will and personality, in concepts of Christian faith, is thus the only possible ground of real individuality, though not the only possible pre-supposition of self-consciousness. But faith in God as will and personality depends upon faith in His power to reveal Himself. The Christian faith in God's self-disclosure, culminating in the revelation of Christ, is thus the basis of the Christian concept of personality and individuality. In terms of this faith man can understand himself as a unity of will which finds its end in the will of God." [7]

In these words the centre of Niebuhr's understanding of man is disclosed. God Himself is will and personality, revealing Himself in creation and in history. In creation and history He reveals Himself as concerned with man, and man becomes what he is, personality and will, by the voluntary act of God's personality, through the personal will of God. Man's personality and will depend upon his voluntary and personal adherence to God, and only in that adherence can they be preserved. The uniqueness of man within creation consists in the relatedness of man and God. Therefore will and personality are no more separable with man than with God. As God's call to men, His revelation in creation and history, is a continuing revelation which cannot be divided into unrelated parts, so man's unity and his uniqueness before God belong to the single individual, to man as a unit in himself. The call of the One God is to the man as one.

The original state of man therefore has, we can see, nothing at all to do with this or that ethical or moral code, but only with the loving will of God revealing itself in creation and history as the cause and the preserver of all that is. This loving will directs itself especially towards man, and sets him above all other creatures as peculiarly bound to God. To keep this truth unqualified and clear, Niebuhr has continually guarded himself against every attempt, Reformation or modern, to deduce from the doctrine of creation specific regulations, either ethical or social.

"In a religion of revelation, the unveiling of the eternal purpose and will, underlying the flux and evanescence of the world, is expected; and the expectation is fulfilled in personal and social-historical experience.

"From the standpoint of an understanding of human nature, the significance of a religion of revelation lies in the fact that both the transcendence of God over, and his intimate relation to, the world are equally emphasized. He is more completely transcendent than the eternity of mystic faith. Mysticism always regards the final depth of human consciousness as in some sense identical with the eternal order, and believes that men may know God if they penetrate deeply enough into the mystery of their own being. But on the other hand the transcendent God of Biblical faith makes Himself known in the finite and historical world. The finite world is not, because of its finiteness, incapable of entertaining comprehensible revelation of the incomprehensible God. The most important characteristic of a religion of revelation is this two-fold emphasis upon the transcendence of God and upon His intimate relation to the world. In this divine transcendence the spirit of man finds a home in which it can understand its stature of freedom. But there it also finds the limits of its freedom, the judgment which is spoken against it and, ultimately, the mercy which makes such a judgment sufferable. God's creation of, and relation to, the world on the other hand prove that human finiteness and involvement in flux are essentially good and not evil. A religion of revelation is thus alone able to do justice to both the freedom and the finiteness of man and to understand the character of the evil in him." [8]

It now becomes wholly clear that faith is set by Niebuhr as one of the two poles necessary for human self-knowledge. It is equally clear that *faith* has for him a very specific meaning, for faith is linked to revelation. Niebuhr never supposes that man by some mystic immersion into himself recognizes the divine within him, and so exalts himself. That is excluded not only by Niebuhr's interest in the other pole, society, but also by the certainty that it is God who reveals Himself and manifests Himself as transcendent; God who of His own will approaches man.

But Niebuhr certainly does not accept the conclusion which might be drawn from Bultmann's writings that man when he is confronted by the divine revelation finds his true self. For Niebuhr, it is God Himself in the divine revelation who brings man into close communion with Himself so that man does not, like Adam, hide himself behind the trees of his finitude and creatureliness, but understands the nature of the evil in himself. Confronted by the revelation of God, what man finds is not himself but his sin.

The absolute necessity of both poles of the original state of man is especially clear at the point where we are apparently concerned with only one pole, faith. Revelation itself allows no withdrawal of man into his solitariness, without damage to the personal character of the relatedness of God and man.

"The revelation of God to man is always a twofold one, a personal-individual revelation, and a revelation in the context of social-historical experience. Without the public and historical revelation the private experience of God would remain poorly defined and subject to caprice. Without the private revelation of God, the public and historical revelation would not gain credence. Since all men have, in some fashion, the experience of a reality beyond themselves, they are able to entertain the more precise revelations of the character and purpose of God as they come to them in the most significant experiences of prophetic history. Private revelation is, in a sense, synonymous with "general" revelation, without the presuppositions of which there could be no "special" revelation. It is no less universal for being private. Private revelation is the testimony in the consciousness of every person that his life touches a reality beyond himself, a reality deeper and higher than the system of nature in which he stands." [9]

Niebuhr is sure that the relatedness between God and the individual man wholly excludes any possibility of a mystic or private tête-a-tête with God. What God says to man personally brings man into relatedness with the whole world around him and gives him his place in it. Man's obedient answer to the loving call of God is the realization that here and now *in nomine Domini* he is obligated to serve the society of men. Through the divine revelation, man is set in his place, in his proper and original state; he is told personally what is valid both in itself and universally. The revelation in creation and history reveals the reality which man has universally experienced. But without revelation man does not accept this real situation as the original, personally willed plan of the loving God. Without revelation, man would face his situation either with indifference or with rejection.

We should also note that individual action for the sake of society as a whole has at bottom no other ground than faith that both the individual and society are created for relatedness with God. Hence faith, in the specific sense in which Niebuhr uses it, and society cannot be regarded as two equally significant and equally important poles. Nor can society be regarded by the individual as on a lower level than his private existence, as something therefore which he may use to satisfy and please himself. On the contrary, God's revelation requires man, if his life is to have any meaning, to take his true place in society so that society may not be an unrelated mass of individuals but a true community.

This point becomes clearer as Niebuhr goes on to speak of

conscience and the commands of God (a subject often treated wholly independently of a dogmatic theology based on revelation).

"The significance of the Biblical interpretation of conscience lies precisely in this, that a universal human experience, the sense of being commanded, placed under obligation and judged is interpreted as a relation between God and man in which it is God who makes demands and judgments upon man. Such an interpretation of a common experience is not possible without the presuppositions of the Biblical faith. But once accepted the assumption proves to be the only basis of a correct analysis of all the factors involved in the experience; for it is a fact that man is judged and yet there is no vantage point in his own life, sufficiently transcendent, from which the judgment can take place." [10]

There is for Niebuhr no possible separation of man and society, since society and man exist by the will of God. And equally there is no place in the life of the individual where man can take a stand over against society in order to determine objectively and to judge his relation to society. It is God who directs the individual man and so all men. God Himself alone judges the ways of man in his relationships. Unquestionably then man receives those commands which we call ethical or moral only as they are derivable from his true station, a position determined by the polarity of faith and society.

For Niebuhr, the turning of God towards man and the relatedness between men which is its result are the foundation of all theological thinking. This conviction is clearly manifest in his view of revelation. He can never admit that, apart from the coming of Christ, the relation between God and man is completely broken. But neither does he accept a pantheistic mysticism nor the liberal view of an unbroken and continuous relation between God and man. The former seems to him both to contradict actual human experience and also to disparage the greatness and breadth of the divine revelation. The latter he considers still more dangerous because it fails to recognize the greatness of the conquest of human sin by God in the completion upon the cross of the whole revelation of the nature of God's love, and also because it refuses to admit the whole abyss of human sin as the voluntary rejection of total personal dependence upon God.

The voluntary and personal element in revelation is definitive for Niebuhr. The fact that God as Person and Will wills to be united with man as a person who wills never allows Niebuhr to engage in the dangerous discussion of universal versus special revelation, or to reject the one in favor of the other. He can see the reality of revelation only as God's perpetual self-disclosure to men. The *what* of revelation, its specific content, a *revelatio quae*, is always far less important than the *He* who is revealed and His purpose in revealing. It is not how and where God is revealed which is decisive for Niebuhr, but God's act in behalf of men, the revealing of His personal and loving will so that man on his side can by his loving response stand voluntarily and truly in relation to God. It is clear that Niebuhr is not thinking of the doctrine of God's revelation as a content. He sees the fissures in the relatedness of God and man today and he is afraid. In fear he confronts the fact of man's rejection of dependence upon God, and so first comes to accept the reality of the divine revelation as God-given. As sinner, Niebuhr knows his need of revelation.

"The general revelation of personal human experience, the sense of being confronted with a 'wholly other' at the edge of human consciousness, contains three elements, two of which are not too sharply defined, while the third is not defined at all. The first is the sense of reverence for a majesty and of dependence upon an ultimate source of being. The second is the sense of moral obligation laid upon one from beyond oneself and of moral unworthiness before a judge. The third, most problematic of the elements in religious experience, is the longing for forgiveness. . . . The first, the sense of dependence upon a reality greater and more ultimate than ourselves, gains the support of another form of 'general' revelation, the content of which is expressed in the concept of the Creator and the creation. Faith concludes that the same 'Thou' who confronts us in our personal experience is also the source and Creator of the whole world. The second element in personal religion, the experience of judgment, gains support from the prophetic-Biblical concept of judgment in history. The whole of history is seen as validation of the truth in the personal experience that God stands over against us as our judge. The third element, the longing for reconciliation after this judgment (and it must be regarded provisionally as a longing rather than an assurance), becomes the great issue of the Old Testament interpretation of life. The question is: is God merciful as well as just? And if He is merciful, how is His mercy related to His justice? This is the question which hovers over the whole of Biblical religion. Because Christian faith believes the final answer to this ultimate question to be given in Christ, it regards the revelation in Christ as final revelation, beyond which there can be no further essential revelation. For this reason it speaks of Christ 'as the express image of his person.' Here the whole depth and mystery of the divine are finally revealed.

"In these three types of revelation God becomes specifically defined as Creator, Judge and Redeemer. It is significant that each term represents a definition of divine transcendence in increasingly specific and sharply delineated terms; and yet in each the relation to the world is preserved." [11]

Niebuhr has here, almost in Schleiermacher's fashion, defined the concepts of a general, yes even a universal revelation; but he has used the words of the special revelation in the Bible and synthesized the universal with the special under the three attributes given in divine revelation: creator, judge, redeemer. These attributes of God correspond precisely with what we have sought to express regarding man's situation: the original state, disorder and restoration. Niebuhr would at any cost deny two differing types of revelation so wholly disconnected that a general revelation proclaims something quite different from the special revelation. On the contrary, he knows only one theme of revelation: God coming to men. The three aspects of general revelation both in the personal experience of the individual and in the historical-social experience of mankind as a whole are supported, elaborated and deepened by what the Bible proclaims as creation, as the history of Israel in the world, and as redemption in and through Christ.

Niebuhr would never at any time admit that there was ever any man or any section of the world which could lie outside God's activity, which God's loving revelation would not reach. The universality of revelation which shines out in Paul's speech on Mars Hill moves Niebuhr to assert that all which exists and is valid does not exist or have validity in itself, but can exist and be valid only in the relatedness of God, man and society. Nothing therefore can be ultimately real in itself, significant and sufficient in itself, but only as it is bound to the personal and voluntary turning of God to man as manifested in creation.

But such a belief does not permit any lapse into a pantheistic monism—quite the contrary. Precisely the personal, voluntary act in the divine revelation means that the transcendence of God and God's turning to men are sharply differentiated. They are combined in God's revealed purpose. The nature of God as love is experienced precisely because as the "wholly other" He turns toward man to relate man to Himself.

"Faith in the transcendent God, as revealed in personal experience and in the character of the whole creation, is the ground upon which the Biblical historical revelation is built up; and this revelation is concerned with the two other attributes of God to man, His judgment and His mercy."[12]

a. The Marks of Man's Original State as Ordered by God

We now must consider more closely what it means for man that he was destined by God for relatedness to God and his fellowmen. We must ask what marks of this original state persist in man as man. We must look at the image of man as it appears when it is fitted into the order of creation. Niebuhr so presents it in three aspects of human nature.

"(1) [The Christian view of man] emphasizes the height of self-transcendence in man's spiritual stature in its doctrine of 'image of God.'

(2) It insists on man's weakness, dependence and finiteness, on his involvement in the necessities and contingences of the

natural world, without, however, regarding this finiteness as, of itself, a source of evil in man. In its purest form the Christian view of man regards man as a unity of God-likeness and creatureliness in which he remains a creature even in the highest spiritual dimensions of his existence and may reveal elements of the image of God even in the lowliest aspects of his natural life.

(3) It affirms that the evil in man is a consequence of his inevitable though not necessary unwillingness to acknowledge his dependence, to accept his finiteness and to admit his insecurity, an unwillingness which involves him in the vicious circle of accentuating the insecurity from which he seeks escape." [13]

When we try to characterize, according to this summary, the marks of man's nature and place in the plan of God, we see at once that all three points refer not to immanent human traits but to the position of man as it is determined by the relationships with which he deals in his activities and aims. Further, the second point depends on the first and the third on the second. The first point defines our bond to God, the second asserts, as the necessary condition of human existence, the close, inescapable relation to others which results from the bond to God and which is good as created. The last presents the behavior of men as a denial of both these relationships.

In Niebuhr's elaboration of these three points we shall find further clarification of the marks of God's plan for man. The Christian view of man which Niebuhr sets forth shows the specific characteristics of the state in which man can live an ordered and meaningful life in his double involvement, his relatedness to God and fellowmen. Man's response ought to be the complete acceptance and the full use of his situation.

"The Biblical view is that the finiteness, dependence and the insufficiency of man's mortal life are facts which belong to God's plan of creation and must be accepted with reverence and humility." [14]

Niebuhr states that God created man for communion with God and his fellowmen. God therefore wills that man is not to be satisfied in himself because he then would be incapable of relatedness in love. Man cannot and ought not to find fulfillment in himself. If he is unrelated, he is not a complete man. The Bible pronounces this position of dependence, which man finds so irritating, to be good and meaningful—not unsatisfactory and evil.

"The fragmentary character of human life is not regarded as evil in Biblical faith because it is seen from the perspective of a centre of life and meaning in which each fragment is related to the plan of the whole, to the will of God." [15]

Whoever refuses to confess the Creator God, in the sense of recognizing man's dependence as necessary for human fulfillment, has a wholly wrong concept of man. What appears in itself as senseless incompleteness because of man's partial vision, must be viewed from the whole which is centred in the will of God. Then meaning and significance become possible. The nature of man designed by God's will requires being related to a context to give it meaning, and the centre of the context lies in God and not in man.

Since it is the loving, and therefore the personal and voluntary creative act of God which has set man in his place and looks for man's affirming answer, the relatedness of man does not mean the loss of freedom of personality, nor the total absorption into a greater whole which Pantheism seeks. On the contrary for Niebuhr, personality and will as signs of a relative freedom are the presuppositions and marks of man's bond to his Creator. What is asked of man is a voluntary, loving acceptance of his station and a fitting of himself to that station. Isolation is the voluntary rejection of the order of creation and is therefore disobedient, sinful disorder.

"The whole import of the Christian doctrine of creation for the Christian view of man is really comprehended in the Christian concept of individuality. The individual is conceived as a creature of infinite possibilities which cannot be fulfilled within terms of this temporal existence. But his salvation never means the complete destruction of his creatureliness and absorption into the divine. On the other hand, though finite individuality is never regarded as of itself evil, its finiteness, including the finiteness of the mind, is never obscured. The self, even in the highest reaches of its self-consciousness, is still the finite self, which must regard the pretensions of universality, to which idealistic philosophies for instance tempt it, as a sin. It is always a self, anxious for its life and its universal perspectives, qualified by its 'here and now' relation to a particular body. Though it surveys the whole world and is tempted to regard its partial transcendence over its body as proof of its candidature for divinity, it remains in fact a very dependent self." [16]

This elucidation of man's uniqueness within the whole creation, and of the nature of the "image of God" in man gives Niebuhr's starting point for his interpretation of man. Man by his peculiar relation to God is raised above pure creature-hood which is wholly conditioned by nature so that he can survey the created world of which he is a part. And this survey includes himself as well as the totality of other creatures and the world. Man's "qualified self-transcendence," as Niebuhr calls it in a somewhat dangerous and misleading phrase, allows man to see world-wide connections and to know the purely chronological pageant of history. (This point we shall later need to consider more fully.) This qualified transcendence, created in the divine order as the basis for man's loving response to the possibility of relatedness which God reveals to him, also gave to man the possibility which is a continual temptation, the possibility of considering himself an independent centre of life and meaning, freed from dependence upon God. He then forgets entirely his creaturely limitations and ignores the fact that he is conditioned by nature and by his whole environment.

But here it is of first importance to remember that this potentiality of qualified self-transcendence is wholly willed by God and therefore is in itself good. The recognition of this truth opens to man the possibility of using this potentiality to the full as a creative force. This God-given human power, by which God has set man in a special position among the creatures, is the centre of the divinely ordered position of man in nature and history. But it is also the spot where man's voluntary disorder, sin, arises. Therefore it is here that the re-ordering, the restoration, of man must take place. We have therefore every reason to deal with it more fully.

b. The Nature of Man's Original State as Ordered by God

Niebuhr attempts to gain clarity in regard to the nature of the original state of man by the use of an old theological concept, *justitia originalis*. We must concede at once that this use gives rise to difficulties. The concept, taken from legal usage, has been employed through centuries of theological thinking. But it serves better to describe a static condition, and it could mean an attribute of *essentia pura*. It can if required be applied to an unexistential attitude of man. It certainly is not an adequate term for what Niebuhr sees as God's dynamic destining of man, that is for man's active, existential relatedness. Nevertheless, the choice of this term is not arbitrary nor accidental, for it is directly indicative of the contrast which exists between God's original design for man and man's behavior, man's voluntary distorting of that design.

Niebuhr begins, in order to establish a legal basis for his discussion of "original righteousness," by combatting an interpretation of the human situation and of human competence which seems to him false. We are reminded of what was said earlier of general revelation and the three elements in it which Niebuhr found especially important. One of these related to conscience and that is here dealt with again—and dealt with polemically.

"The sense of a conflict between what man is and ought to be finds universal expression, even though the explanations of the conflict are usually contradictory and confused.

"This universal testimony of human experience is the most persuasive refutation of any theory of human depravity which denies that man has any knowledge of the good which sin has destroyed. It is true of course, as Christian faith declares, that any human statement of the blessedness and perfection which are man's proper state and nature, are themselves coloured by sin, so that Christ, as the second Adam, is required to restore the image of the first Adam as he was before the Fall. The reason why there is a heightened sense of sin in Christianity is because the vision of Christ heightens the contrast between what man is truly and what he has become; and destroys the prestige of normality which sinful forms of life periodically achieve in the world. Yet faith in Christ could find no lodging place in the human soul, were it not uneasy about the contrast between its true and its present state; though this same faith in Christ also clarifies that contrast. Men who have fallen deeply into the wretchedness of sin are never easy in their minds; but their uneasiness is frequently increased by some vivid reminder of the innocency of their childhood or the aspirations of their youth.

"There are no forms of disease or corruption, short of death, which do not reveal something of the healthful structure which they have corrupted. The blind eye is still an eye, though it may be completely sightless." [17]

When Niebuhr speaks of this *justitia originalis*, he speaks of it always as only a possibility. But it is just this possibility which is to him so important. The contrast between what is and what ought to be must never be forgotten. Niebuhr certainly never expects to rescue some fragment of evident worth out of the conglomerate mass of sinful man's corruption, but he does insist that the relatedness created by God, created good, and as God's creation never to be wholly destroyed, has still a recognizable effect in human existence, even in man's sinful withdrawal from his Creator.

From the foregoing it should be clear that Niebuhr (he least of all) will not contend for any actual remainder of goodness in man which man can plead against God, apart from his relatedness to God. On the contrary, the gulf between what is and what ought to be can only reveal with utmost clarity the greatness of the love of God and the total dependence of man upon God, even in his sin. It makes plain that man is on the one hand free and endowed with will; on the other hand he can never fully escape from life-giving relatedness to God. The unfaithfulness of man can never bring to naught the faithfulness of God. This is Niebuhr's belief. And because this faithfulness of God is a faithfulness directed towards man, it does not permit man to rest content in his sin. Again we see clearly that no statement of Niebuhr's can be understood apart from his fundamental assertion of the relatedness between God, man and society.

And we also see why Niebuhr so stresses the existing tension and why in what follows he presents a further distinction in clarification of his position. He separates the essential nature of man and man's original righteousness.

"It is impossible to do justice to the concept of the image of God and to the perfection of that image before the Fall without making a distinction between the essential nature of man and the virtue of conformity to that nature. Nothing can change the essential nature and structure, just as blindness of the eye does not remove the eye from the human anatomy. Not even the destruction of the eye can change the fact that the human anatomy requires two eyes. On the other hand the freedom of man creates the possibility of actions which are contrary to and in defiance of the requirements of this essential nature. This fact justifies the distinction between the essential structure and nature, and the virtue of conformity to it. Man may lose his virtue and destroy the proper function of his nature but he can do so only by availing himself of one of the elements in that nature, namely his freedom." [18]

The original state of man as willed by God with its consequences for men has here been more accurately diagrammed. Man is a being with a nature determined by God, an essential nature, the elements of which correspond to the requirements of communion with God and society. One element of this nature, man's freedom, permits him either to persevere in the virtue of conformity with this essential nature—such a choice would continue his original righteousness—or to reject voluntarily such conformity, and therefore to rebel against God's design. Such rebellion does not achieve the complete destruction of man's essential nature but it dooms man to the tension between what ought to be and that which is actually before his eyes. This tension produces a "bad conscience." The tension is brought into clear light through the revelation in Christ, but it was not created by that revelation. It belongs to the actual existence of man as he is.

What ought to be can also appear to men as law, the so-called "natural law," which Niebuhr now discusses.

"The virtue and perfection which correspond to the first element of [man's peculiar] nature is usually designated as the natural law. It is the law which defines the proper performance of his functions, the normal harmony of his impulses and the normal social relation between himself and his fellows within the limitations of the natural order. Since every natural function of man is qualified by his freedom and since a 'law' defining normality is necessary only because of his freedom, there is always an element of confusion in thus outlining a law of nature. It has nevertheless a tentative validity; for it distinguishes the obvious requirements of his nature as a creature in the natural order from the special requirements of his nature as free spirit." [19]

The state peculiar to man, who is on the one hand a part of the creatures confined within the limitations of nature and finitude, and who on the other hand can survey and know this limitation so that he is not only limited but also free within this limitation, finds its appropriate fulfillment if man, as destined by God and by Him destined for society, finds his place in relatedness to God and his fellowmen. To this true position corresponds the second element of the original righteousness, which Niebuhr describes under three aspects, faith, love and hope—all values of relationship.

"Faith in the providence of God is a necessity of freedom because, without it, the anxiety of freedom tempts man to seek a self-sufficiency and self-mastery incompatible with his dependence upon forces which he does not control. Hope is a particular form of that faith. It deals with the future as a realm where infinite possibilities are realized and which must be a realm of terror if it is not under the providence of God; for in that case it would stand under either a blind fate or pure caprice. The knowledge of God is thus not a supernatural grace which is a 'further gift' beyond man's essential nature. It is the requirement of his nature as free spirit.

"Love is both an independent requirement of this same freedom and a derivative of faith. Love is a requirement of freedom because the community to which man is impelled by his social nature is not possible to him merely upon the basis of his gregarious impulse. In his freedom and uniqueness each man stands outside of, and transcends, the cohesions of nature and the uniformities of mind which bind life to life. Since men are separated from one another by the uniqueness and individuality of each spirit, however closely they may be bound together by ties of nature, they cannot relate themselves to one another in terms which will do justice to both the bonds of nature and the freedom of their spirit if they are not related in terms of love. In love spirit meets spirit in the depth of the innermost essence of each. The cohesions of nature are qualified and transmuted by this relationship, for the other self ceases to be merely an object, serviceable to the self because of affinities of nature and reason. It is recognized as not merely object but as itself a subject, as a unique centre of life and purpose. This 'I' and 'Thou' relationship is impossible without the presupposition of faith for two reasons: (1) Without freedom from anxiety man is so enmeshed in the vicious circle of egocentricity, so concerned about himself, that he cannot release himself for the adventure of love. (2) Without relation to God, the world of freedom in which spirit must meet spirit is so obscured that human beings constantly sink to the level of things in the human imagination. The injunction, 'love thy neighbor as thyself' is therefore properly preceded both by the commandment, 'love the Lord thy God,' and by the injunction, 'be not anxious.'" [20]

We see now why Niebuhr spoke of a God-given original state of man, willed by God, and not of laws decreed by God. If there were merely a question of divine laws by which man could rightly direct his activity, man would remain fundamentally self-directed.

But because it is God who created man qualified for his destined position of relatedness, who guarantees to man through inner communion with Him protection and therefore freedom from sinful self-centredness, God makes man free to create true relatedness with his fellowmen in the bond of love which allows the other to be truly himself. Only so is true humanity possible, and only so can there be true community in society.

From God, life flows out and touches man and leads him into society. True community is impossible without true relatedness to God. It is equally impossible that this true relatedness should not create true community. It must therefore be expressly stated that the nature of man cannot be apprehended apart from his uniqueness, and that man unlike the other creatures cannot satisfy himself with unthinking subsistence. He knows himself, even as he stands within the limitations of nature yet transcends them, to be a being with a twofold obligation, to God and to his fellowmen.

So faith and society are the poles of the original state of man. A disturbance of this dual polarity produces a disturbance in the nature of man, and the result of that disturbance is the gulf between what man ought to be according to his essential nature and what he must know himself to be in his confusion and disconnectedness. The tension is inherent and continuous, not a total opposition between two separate and unrelated worlds. Man's knowledge of his essential nature does not come to him through revelation only, "vertically from above." It is a knowledge which conscience has of the essence of humanity.

But more specific inquiry into the ground of this knowledge makes clear that it is not a possession, an immanent capacity of man, since its content is man's relatedness. The knowledge which conscience has asserts that man is essentially bound to God. But this knowledge which conscience has cannot itself be the bond, for it belongs itself to the fragmentariness of sinning man. The knowledge therefore is not excepted from human uncertainty and doubt; it is not in itself "wholeness of knowledge," a knowledge of perfection.

"The consciousness and memory of an original perfection in the self-as-transcendent must not be regarded as the possession of perfection. The fact is that the self-as-transcendent always assumes, mistakenly, that its present ability to judge and criticize the undue and unjust claims of the self in a previous action is a guarantee of its virtue in a subsequent action. This is not the case, for when the self acts it always uses the previous transcendent perspective partly as a 'rationalization' and 'false front' for its interested action." [21]

Since the existence of the original righteousness is always prior to any human activity of thought, word or deed, it is obviously outside the life and activity of men, an *a priori* transcendent to them. We come then inevitably to the question of the Fall as the shattering of man's original righteousness.

"In placing the consciousness of 'original righteousness' in a moment of the self which transcends history, though not outside of the self which is in history, it may be relevant to observe that this conforms perfectly to the myth of the Fall when interpreted symbolically. The myth does not record any actions of Adam which were sinless, though much is made in theology of the perfection he had before the Fall. Irenaeus, with geater realism than most theologians, observes that the period was very brief, sin following almost immediately upon his creation. Adam was sinless before he acted and sinful in his first recorded action. His sinlessness, in other words, preceded his first significant action and his sinfulness came to light in that action. This is a symbol for the whole of human history. The original righteousness of man stands, as it were, outside of history. Yet it is in the man who is in history, and when sin comes it actually borrows from this original righteousness. For the pretension of sin is that its act is not in history but an act of impartiality, a deed of eternity." [22]

Niebuhr therefore never assigns the *justitia originalis* to any particular constituent part of man. It acts as the directing force of man's essential nature. Similarly, Niebuhr can give no fixed chronological moment at which the original righteousness existed as an historical fact. Original righteousness exists only as a constant corrective in man's conscience by which his doing and leaving undone is always judged and declared imperfect; and man's sin appears perpetually in the moment in which he desires to claim independence and perfection for his own action.

Thus original righteousness always escapes the immanent limit of history, yet the historical action of men is always judged by its contrast to this transcendency, because the spaceless and timeless *justitia originalis* persists in the knowledge of the human conscience—not as a possession of men, but as a summons to him to return to God. It is an imperishable element of that returning.

So Niebuhr resists any desire to state in definite terms the nature and content of the original righteousness, as the doctrine of the ordinances of creation attempts to do. He offers no summary of natural law. Likewise, but more specifically, he makes it clear that he is not discussing a fixed possession of man, neither an ability nor even a cognizance and knowledge which would enable men to behave and act merely according to rules. No, the content and nature of the original righteousness is love; that is, it consists in man's loving placement of himself within the bond uniting him to God and to his fellowmen, the bond which itself had its source in the original order of creation. Only faith, hope and love are valid to characterize this original righteousness, because they are not static terms describing the nature of man but dynamic expressions of the direction of man's activity. We must continually return to this point.

"Love is thus the end term of any system of morals. It is the moral requirement in which all schemes of justice are fulfilled and negated. They are fulfilled because the obligation of life to life is more fully met in love than is possible in any scheme of equity and justice. They are negated because love makes an end of the nicely calculated less and more of structures of justice. It does not carefully arbitrate between the needs of the self and of the other, since it meets the needs of the other without concern for the self." [23]

Original righteousness then always points away from the capacities of man to his need of communion with God. By its nature, which is love, it is directed to other men, to action in and for society; and therefore it demonstrates ever more clearly the indispensability of a living bond with God in faith.

Since the original state of man involves the capacity and the necessity of having a continuing, living relatedness to God and to fellowmen, the poles of that original state for the individual man are faith and society. The centre of the original state lay in this unique position and nature of man. It therefore always transcends every individual life and makes self-satisfaction and self-containment impossible. The original righteousness has a transcendent character and can never find a fulfillment within the limits of man's self-will and selfishness. It can be fulfilled only in the framework of man's relatedness to God and fellowmen.

Every view of man which ignores the established pattern of man's original state, and ignores also therefore God who established it, must miss the reality of man. Every anthropology which thinks it can apprehend man by its definitions and propositions will fall apart because man is not a closed entity. His nature and destiny—to use Niebuhr's title—is his aptitude for relationships, for his destined relatedness.

Niebuhr believes that the emergence of this concept of man from the wrappings of some thousands of more or less sharp definitions occurred in the Renaissance and Reformation, since both, though in different ways and each only partially, broke the frozen mediaeval image of man. Niebuhr therefore proposes to set forth the new image of man, which must be a combination and amalgamation of the two contradictory views of the Renaissance and the Reformation.

Renaissance and Reformation each saw one side of human reality better than the Middle Ages had been able to see it. But both were so impressed by the one side discovered and so bound to it that they could not see the other side at all, still less recognize its importance. But since the insight and the blindness of the Renaissance and the Reformation are mutually opposite, Niebuhr finds a possibility and a necessity for a new anthropology which shall fit together the two contrasting discoveries and so correct the one-sided blindness of both with its corresponding errors.

The Renaissance saw human nature and history as a realm of unlimited possibilities and felt that the Middle Ages had not done justice to human freedom and destiny. But the blind confidence of the Renaissance was wrong, since it assumed that the possibility of good would progressively overcome the possibilities of evil. The Renaissance saw neither the cause nor the significance of human sin.

On the other hand the Reformation was obsessed by the idea, which it had newly discovered, that no distinction between good men and bad could have real significance because in the eyes of God such a distinction did not exist. The Reformation was governed by the insight, which is both true and essential, that all men without distinction stand in need of the merciful love of God for their forgiveness and redemption. But exclusive concern with this insight kept the Reformation from recognizing the monstrous social (in the widest sense of the word) significance of sin. Lacking this further insight and realizing that human activity in the world could never have a truly decisive character, the Reformation ignored the possibility, God-given to God-created man, of achieving positive constructive work in the world, and the consequent obligation, God-imposed on man, to undertake such work. It was this possibility of constructive work which had become uniquely important to the Renaissance.

In considering the Reformation we must not of course generalize too widely. It must be admitted that the Lutherans were much more one-sided, and that Calvinism constantly made efforts to do justice to man's obligations in society. Yet it can be said that on the whole Reformation and Renaissance both overlooked one of the two poles of man's original state. The Renaissance could not recognize nor value either faith as man's voluntary acceptance of his dependence upon God nor the effect of faith which is the out-going activity of the individual in free love for his fellowmen. The Renaissance failed to see that dependence upon God did not mean enslavement, and it recognized still less that unbounded freedom did not mean unlimited progressive good for man.

The Reformation overlooked the other pole of man's original state, society. It did not realize that the same God who on the one hand judges us not according to our works and our desserts, but according to His grace and its acceptance in faith, also on the other hand by His loving grace directs us towards our fellowmen in society in order that we may learn there the effects of our sins, and use there among our fellowmen the new God-given powers in the way ordered by God from the beginning. Only so could the world be prevented from falling into anarchic disorder through the irresponsible withdrawal of Christians from it, and become new in true community. The Reformation did not accept seriously the word that God so loved the *world* that He gave His only begotten Son that all who believe on Him may not perish but have eternal life.

The Renaissance's just criticism of the world-denying spiritual tyranny of the Middle Ages obscured the true significance of faith as a necessary pole of man's original state. But the Reformation's equally justified attack upon the church of the Middle Ages as being worldly to the point of identifying itself with the world so that it seemed to have no longer any knowledge of an eschatological end of this world, prevented the recognition of society as the equally indispensible pole, with all the ensuing consequences of such recognition.

The inadequacy of both these attitudes had serious effects for the next era, in which significantly the error of the Renaissance had by far the greater influence. But the errors must not prevent the recognition of the much more important true insights of Renaissance and Reformation. These Niebuhr will combine. Both faith and society, God's grace and man's will to build, combined as mutually requisite, serve to bring to men of faith within society the radical restoration of man's original state as ordered by God.

"Both Renaissance and Reformation explored complexities of human nature beyond the limits understood in the 'medieval synthesis.' But the discoveries of each stood in contradiction to each other. Some of the confusions of modern culture about human nature arise from this unresolved contradiction. Others are derived from the fact that the Renaissance triumphed over the Reformation so completely that the insights of the latter were preserved only in a few backwaters and eddies of modern culture." [24]

We have seen that the Christian understanding of man finds the essence and the uniqueness of man in his divinely appointed bond with God and his fellowmen. This relatedness extricates him from the trap of his desire to find satisfaction in himself. We have seen also that the anthropological attempt to understand man apart from his position ordered by God ends in failure. But we need to consider further how the modern understanding of the self has developed.

The Greek view of man presents a combination of Platonic, Aristotelian and Stoic philosophy with the insight of Greek tragedy. The contribution of philosophy was the emphasis and exclusive value laid upon the rational gifts of man, an emphasis which led necessarily to clear-cut dualism. The witness of tragedy (so little understood by the modern world) demanded the belief that the conflicts of life are produced by more and mightier powers than pure rational dualism would accept; that life itself is at war with itself unremittingly and inescapably. The self-limited strength of disciplined order fights the unlimited strength of the original life-force which is continually breaking out and can never be met on equal terms or excluded. Antiquity's view of man is tragic, although in late antiquity the note of resignation sounds, sometimes clearly, sometimes muffled. This is the normal consequence of two contradictory attempts, the one to surmount nature through the higher spirit, the opposite of nature; the other to withdraw one's self wholly from the conflict of life.

That which never appears in antiquity's view of man is exactly what is for us most important, man's relatedness as established in the loving turning of God to men, not blotting out man's personality but making it truly free, and in the loving response of man to the God who directs him to the building of community in society.

Greek tragedy saw man as without defense and hope, on a battlefield where superhuman powers fight and exhaust their fury, where man himself is drawn into the battle and is made responsible for it, where therefore his own task—to be truly a human being—is given up as impossible. Alternately, man in

Greek philosophy is required to break by his own power the inner tension between matter-bound nature and free spirit. Man's unity is thus impossible. The two powers condemn and extinguish each other. Man ceases to be man. If he rises up in conflict against the superhuman powers, he must turn upward to spirit and deny his nature which ties him to the earth below. If he escapes into a wholly natural subsistence, he must then resign his spiritual transcendence which is a part of being a human being.

In antiquity's classical presentation of the two opposite ways of escape from the unbearable tension of human independence, Niebuhr finds the starting point for his exposition of the anti-social results of sin—he calls them later pride and sensuality. With them he begins his discussion.

The modern view of man does not offer anything new or singular in its understanding of man, but rather brings out clearly the accumulated problems. Niebuhr summarizes it as follows:

"The curious compound of classical, Christian and distinctively modern conceptions of human nature, involved in modern anthropology, leads to various difficulties and confusions which may be briefly summarized as follows: (a) The inner contradictions in modern conceptions of human nature between idealistic and naturalistic rationalists; and between rationalists, whether idealistic or naturalistic, and vitalists and romanticists. (b) The certainties about human nature in modern culture which modern history dissipates, particularly the certainty about individuality. (c) The certainties about human nature, particularly the certainty about the goodness of man, which stand in contradiction to the known facts of history." [25]

It is plain that the modern view of man possesses no unity. It is doubly contradictory, including first the contradictions of the opposing schools of philosophy, and second the contradictions between what philosophy accepts as true and the incontrovertible facts of history.

From this brief survey, we see that the whole attempt of man to exalt himself by ignoring his original state ordained by God, and using only his self-knowledge falls to pieces because it cannot fit man into the totality of the world forces which surround and limit him. And this failure destroys not only the relation of man to his environment but equally man's own inner adjustment. The confusion of modern man reveals his inner and his outer unrelatedness. The modern non-religious anthropologies have shown that man when he attempts to know himself becomes involved in contradictions. When he stubbornly denies his bond to God and asserts himself as independent, he transforms the order created by God into disorder—that is the theme which will be further developed in what follows.

But first we must ask ourselves, what is the real significance of this original state of man, Niebuhr's insistence on which so surprised us. We need to speak of an original state of man, decreed by God, because Niebuhr's analysis of human reality has proved that the personality of man and his whole existence displays a character essentially out-reaching with a twofold bond to God and to fellowmen, and that therefore the two poles essential to the true state of the individual man are God and society. But this reality, demonstrated by the knowledge which conscience has of what ought to be true about men, is never anywhere realized. It cannot be preserved, still less can it be created by human action. So much was made clear in Niebuhr's interpretation of the myth of the Fall. The reality therefore must belong to an original state given by God, the Creator of all human life and must be prior to man's knowledge and possession of himself. From this original state, because of his desire for unrelated independence, man has fallen into disorder. To it he must be restored if he is to live meaningfully, according to his destiny.

2. *Man's Disorder*

a. The Distortion of the Image of Man

The modern man, because he believes himself able to create order by his own powers and abilities, believes also that he has no need of an order divinely decreed for him, and even supposes that he must reject any such order as a hampering brake on his progress. We therefore need first to explore the constituent elements of human creative power; for their harmony is a necessity if man is to establish his own order, and their discord makes order impossible.

From the beginning of human achievement, vitality and form present themselves as the phenomenological areas where the problem of nature and spirit is manifest. Here again, Niebuhr seeks a new position in anthropological phenomenology. Refusing to be satisfied with abstract reflections upon the unity of human nature, he seeks to comprehend its operative effects, its active manifestations. Thus at the very beginning he is able to consider being and action in relation rather than separately. For Niebuhr, man exists in his activity and acts in accordance with his being. The whole course of Niebuhr's thinking is really determined by this refusal to allow any division between the being and the behavior of men, by his insistence on their indissoluble unity.

Niebuhr then distinguishes four elements of human creativity:

"(1) The vitality of nature (its impulses and drives).

(2) The forms and unities of nature—that is the determinations of instincts and the forms of natural cohesion and natural differentiation.

(3) The freedom of spirit within limits to transcend natural forms and redirect the vitalities [or to repress them].

(4) . . . The forming capacity of spirit, its ability to create a new realm of coherence and order.

"All these four factors are involved in human creativity and by implication in human destructiveness."[26]

Here two significant points should be kept in mind. First, these factors of human creativity are not discrete, but organically connected. Niebuhr does not separate energy from the achievement of form, but he distinguishes between the drive of nature with its own forms on the one hand, and the ability of spirit on the other hand to extricate itself partially from the context of nature, and to achieve its effect upon the natural behavior of humanity, in similar fashion as a formative power. Human creativity exists therefore within this reciprocal relation in which neither element can dispense with the other.

Secondly, it is equally important to remember that Niebuhr does not label man's creativity as in itself good or bad, but only asserts that all four factors are present in both the creative and the destructive capacity of man. He does not believe that our problem is merely how to permit a creative power, good in itself, to work unhampered, as if then all problems of action would vanish. He believes rather that a correct and true ordering of the whole man is required for their solution. It is the inner pattern and structure of human capacity which itself raises the problem of the true inner relationship of the separate formative powers. The problems of man's environment are closely interwoven with man's inner problem, and are dependent upon it for solution.

Secular analyses of man attempt to bring all the factors into correct relation to one another, but they fall into the error of insisting upon a solution which depends on the predominance of one of the two elements, spirit or vitality, instead of on a harmonious combination of both. The result is the complete destruction of harmony. This error of rationalism on the one side and of romanticism on the other operates not merely on a theoretical level. Its effects are social, economic and political, as the close relation of Marxism and Naziism (the latter through Nietzsche) to Romanticism shows.

Niebuhr does not make so full an investigation of these errors and their results merely for the purpose of rejecting them. He is seeking to learn their fundamental character and aim, in which are manifested the nature of man and his desires. He therefore does not begin with an absolute repudiation, but he tries by discussion of differing interpretations to determine the real nature of man. In this discussion, everything depends for him on the fact that his own conception of man does not divide into static being and dynamic action, and thus for him nothing in man can be more correctly derived from or related to one element rather than the other. Actually he puts the main accent on activity and opposes the general philosophical position in which often nothing appears beyond an anthropological ontology.

But Niebuhr is never willing to separate the two. He knows that would be the first fatal step which would inevitably end later in the separation of nature and spirit. These for him belong absolutely together in man. Niebuhr's definition of an individual includes equally nature and spirit. Both are for him the roots of human personality which is "a fruit of both nature and spirit." [27]

"Genuine individuality, embodying both discreteness and uniqueness, is a characteristic of human life. It must consequently be regarded as the product of spirit as well as of nature. Nature supplies particularity but the freedom of the spirit is the cause of real individuality. Man, unlike animal existence, not only has a centre but he has a centre beyond himself. Man is the only animal which can make itself its own object. This capacity for self-transcendence which distinguishes spirit in man from soul (which he shares with animal existence), is the basis of discrete individuality, for this self-consciousness involves consciousness of the world as 'the other.' . . . Human consciousness involves the sharp distinction between the self and the totality of the world. Self-knowledge is thus the basis of discrete individuality.

"Human capacity for self-transcendence is also the basis of human freedom and thereby of the uniqueness of the individual. Human consciousness not only transcends natural process but it transcends itself. It thereby gains the possibility for those endless variations and elaborations of human capacities which characterize human existence." [28]

We must now consider carefully how and why every philosophical attempt has failed to produce in actuality the harmony for which it aimed, why its result was not co-ordination but disorderly conflict. We must notice in this connection how carefully Niebuhr defines the various elements in their functional orbits and particularizes them, without destroying their functional coherence or blurring the nature of individuality. His course is very different from the main stream of the history of thought responsible for the contradictory disorder in the conception of man. For example, Niebuhr blames rationalism not only for its radical separation of matter and spirit, which results in contempt and denial of the physical body; he condemns it also because, influenced by Platonism, it explains the human conflict and tension from the physical alone.

"This inner conflict is an obvious fact which proves that man alone, among all animals, stands in contradiction to himself. The possibility for this contradiction is given by the self-transcendence of the human spirit, the fact that man is not only soul, as unity of the body, but spirit, as capacity to transcend both the body and the soul. But Plato does not recognize that the anarchic impulses which the 'soul' brings into subjection are more than mere bodily impulses. They are impulses which have been given their freedom by the fact that man is spirit as well as nature. Plato thus falsely identifies anarchy with bodily impulse. Answering the question 'Whence come wars and fightings and factions?' he answers erroneously, 'Whence but from the body and the lusts of the body.' "[29]

The protest of Romanticism against the error of Rationalism is many sided. It is not limited to asserting the independent goodness, the superlative goodness, of the vital impulse, as Nietzsche did. It also denies the capacity of spirit to master the vital impulse and pillories the dishonesty of spirit in making such a claim and attempting to have it allowed. Rationalism condemned the physical as evil; Romanticism puts spirit under the same condemnation. Bergson sought in mystical exaltation of the *élan vital* to ascribe to it the capacity of finding harmony in itself. Schopenhauer finally named the moment of will as dominating over the totality of nature and spirit, and uniting them, but he did not recognize how far the will itself is conditioned.

"But romanticism errs not only in the contradictory criticisms which it levels at rationalism in general and idealism in particular. It also errs in interpreting the vitality of man, of which it constitutes itself the champion. Its error consists not so much in reducing that vitality to bio-mechanical proportions as bourgeois naturalism tends to do. Its basic error lies in its effort to ascribe to the realm of the biological and the organic what is clearly a compound of nature and spirit, of biological impulse and rational spiritual freedom. Man is never a simple two-layer affair who can be understood from the standpoint of the bottom layer, should efforts to understand him from the standpoint of the top layer fail. If rationalism tends to depreciate the significance, power, inherent order and unity of biological impulse, romanticism tends to appreciate these without recognizing that human nature knows no animal impulse in its pure form." [30]

Both Rationalism and Romanticism (in close relation to which Niebuhr puts Marxism) fail because they cannot regard man as a unit in tension between two equally basic poles, both together essential to the nature of man, to his individuality. Both Rationalism and Romanticism seek the key to the interpretation of man in one only of the two poles, and hope from that one pole to end man's tension and thereby to understand the essence of humanity.

And if we remind ourselves of what we learned earlier, that only within the order created by the loving command of God is it possible to know man rightly in his true relatedness, then we see that the modern age, true to the inheritance from the Renaissance, is struggling toward the opposite pole, the autonomous individual.

"If Protestantism represents the final heightening of the idea of individuality within terms of the Christian religion, the Renaissance is the real cradle of that very unchristian concept and reality:

the autonomous individual. The Renaissance emphasis upon individual autonomy is partly a reaction to Catholic authoritarianism. Its part in the emancipation of learning from the tyranny of religious dogmatism is so great that most of the uncritical devotees of the 'scientific spirit' of modernity have not discerned the peril in this idea of autonomy. Ostensibly Renaissance thought is a revival of classicism, the authority of which is either set against the authority of Christianity or used to modify the latter. Yet classic thought has no such passion for the individual as the Renaissance betrays. The fact is that the Renaissance uses an idea which could have grown only upon the soil of Christianity. It transplants this idea to the soil of classic rationalism to produce a new concept of individual autonomy which is known in neither classicism nor Christianity." [31]

In the rise of the secular idea of the "autonomous self," therefore, the Biblical teaching of the value of the individual is accepted; but man's relatedness to God and fellowmen, the essential condition of true individuality is denied. A fragment of Biblical thinking has been distorted and utilized for the wholly anthropocentric thought of rational individualism. This explains why the concept of the "autonomous individual" never appears entirely acclimated. Its fate corresponds to its origin. A different, an unphilosophic, movement gave it birth. Economic and social development brought the rise of the middle class which at the time of the Renaissance had already gained power in the Italian city states and at the time of the Enlightenment had spread over most of Europe. The new economic and social situation gave new opportunity to individual initiative.

"The business man developed a form of economic power which depends upon individual initiative and resourcefulness rather than upon hereditary advantages; and which creates dynamic rather than static social relationships. It naturally sees human history as a realm of human decisions rather than of inexorable destiny. In the same way it regards nature as an instrument rather than the master of the human will. The rise of the natural sciences was at first merely a by-product of this sense of human self-reliance, for nature was regarded merely as the mirror of the greatness of man.

But as science gradually contributed to man's actual mastery of natural forces it gave a new impetus of its own to the idea of human self-sufficiency.

"This pride and power of man, who surprises himself by the influence of his decisions upon history and the power of his actions upon nature, who discovers himself as a creator, is subtly merged with the Christian idea of the significance of each man in the sight of God. It is indeed a this-worldly version of the latter." [32]

This passage presents an important insight into the development of human self-knowledge, the origins of which are so complex. It demonstrates that the goal of man's being toward which man himself is striving, that which man himself always desires to gain, corresponds exactly with what God in the beginning designed for man in His decreed order, for man lovingly obedient within his bond to God. God's love which so distinguished man from the rest of creation and summoned him to the mastery over nature, imposed as the single *sine qua non*, as the indispensible condition, that it be man's bond with God which gives him the right to his position and qualifies him for it. Secular thinking does not accept this condition, but the secular self-centred, autonomous individual lays claim to this high position. Now it is the freedom of the spirit which makes it possible for the spirit to win authority in the world over nature and fellowmen. Consequently, the illusion of self-sufficient and self-perfecting autarchy is strengthened. This freedom of the spirit is the gift of God's love which refuses to force man to love in return. Yet man, when relying on himself alone, is not capable of using and preserving authority in freedom. There he has deceived himself.

The consequence has been that man, over-estimating his own power when alone and outside the protecting bond with God the Creator, has torn down the boundary wall which sheltered him against the forces of nature and history and has fallen helpless before them. Chaos resulted, confusion in the mind of man and destruction in human society—exactly as the myth of the tower of Babel tells it. Man suddenly felt himself no match for the assaults of nature and history, and sought—but still by himself—

to win back at any price a protecting wall whose shelter he now missed.

But he did not seek security within the relatedness of God, man and society. Faith and society are not the governing poles of his self-willed search for self-restoration. He turns to the immanent forces of the world and seeks to merge himself fully in them. He cannot by himself attain the right, that is a personal voluntary, relation to these powers—a relatedness such as God had designed and within which He had designed the uniqueness of man in His loving, original order. Man, in the procedure he has chosen to follow, loses himself.

Of course no philosophy and no substitute religion can really fashion or alter the essential being of man. They can, however, obscure man's view of himself so that the self is finally lost because it cannot find itself within the relatedness ordained by God. Nature dissipates the self because it reduces the personal, spiritually conditioned will to fully determined natural antecedents, and so removes man's freedom which is the first requisite for a self. Idealism with its method of abstraction presents us with an ideal self which is incapable of life because it divides the personal unity of natural finitude and spiritual self-transcendence. Hence the spiritualized self loses its relation to physical reality and is detached from its environment. Naturalism denies man's freedom, and idealism his finitude. But the true self is a unity of finitude and freedom in the person who knows himself to be bound.

Niebuhr rightly guards against the assumption that man's confusion is merely an accidental human error. There is in it also the element of voluntary escape from the responsibility for human sin. Man is fleeing from the divine judgment, whether in Naturalism he throws the responsibility on impersonal natural causes or in Idealism labels the involvement in nature as in itself the origin of evil and tries vainly to separate his own humanity from it. But it is man in his unity of finitude and freedom who must be set right with himself and his fellowmen. All these escapes from responsibility only show that man cannot actually exist without the bond to God. Wherever in his sinfulness he seeks to do so, he loses himself and his life as a person.

"Without the presuppositions of the Christian faith the individual is either nothing or becomes everything. In the Christian faith man's insignificance as a creature, involved in the process of nature and time, is lifted into significance by the mercy and power of God in which his life is sustained. But his significance as a free spirit is understood as subordinate to the freedom of God. His inclination to abuse his freedom, to overestimate his power and significance and to become everything is understood as the primal sin. It is because man is inevitably involved in this primal sin that he is bound to meet God first of all as a judge, who humbles his pride and brings his vain imagination to naught." [33]

The breaking of the bond with God and fellowmen resulted in the disintegration of man's self, a disintegration which no human attempt at explanation and solution can cure. On the contrary, such attempts have only aggravated the situation since they obscure in darkness what the facts of history and life thrust into glaring light—that the deepest roots of man's inability to bring his world to order lie in the presumptuous destruction of the original order decreed by God. Therefore the first step back towards restoration and healing must be the acceptance of the divine judgment upon this destruction, upon the original sin of man.

The especial value in all this investigation is Niebuhr's readiness to pursue man's confusion to the end, that is to the point where the bitter verdict of sin and guilt is pronounced. Furthermore, he is not willing to define this confusion as a regrettable mistake on the ethico-moral level, which leaves the essential nature of man more or less undisturbed. Not at all—he traces the break in the relatedness to God and society back to the incurable disintegration of the human being himself. We shall later see that Niebuhr, just because he connects the nature of sin with the nature of man's deepest mode of existence and understands the whole as a problem of right relation, has opened wide possibilities, new and hitherto unheard of, in the area of theology and anthropology, of morals and ethics.

But if Niebuhr is right in seeing that modern man's first step toward improvement should be confession to God, the Judge of his destructive and sinful rebellion, then it is of the deepest and most calamitous significance that man has not taken this step, but is absconding in the opposite direction. Niebuhr finds the most impressive evidence of this in a phenomenon noteworthy in itself, in the "easy conscience" of the modern man.

"The most surprising aspect of the modern man's good conscience is that he asserts and justifies it in terms of the most varied and even contradictory metaphysical theories and social philosophies. The idealist Hegel and the materialist Marx agree in their fundamental confidence in human virtue, disagreeing only in their conception of the period and the social circumstances in which and the method by which his essential goodness is, or is to be, realized." [34]

What is truly astonishing about this good conscience of modern man is the fact that it is not disturbed by historical events which so totally contradict it. Modern man still believes that he can reject as unneeded by him the redemption offered in the Christian message. He does not assert the needlessness flatly; he hides his self-satisfaction behind criticism of the message. Its doctrines are not susceptible of rational proof and are therefore untenable. The teaching on sin presents "a psychopathic aspect of adolescent mentality."

Man's misinterpretation of man, caused by the inner tension of his unrelatedness, reveals its true nature especially in the projection outward of the problem of man's divided personality. Man recognizes evil only outside of himself and insists that treatment must begin there. Niebuhr gives serious consideration to all these attempts at escape and explores them thoroughly.

Modern man in order to evade his own responsibility seeks to ascribe the evil in the world to a great variety of factors in his environment, to the influence of various movements, and especially to individual evil men. But even if he could show that such causes produce confusion in men, he still would never succeed in explaining how evil can enter a good world or men who are really in themselves good.

Clearly the question must be differently put. Man ought to ask how and when evil was actually introduced. Only if this question were answered so that the corollary could be drawn "nature is the source of virtue," could naturalism be defended.

> "The hope of modern culture of eliminating human wrongdoing through the political and economic reorganization stands in more or less confused relation with its other hope of eliminating social evil by more individual methods of return to the simple harmony of nature. The modern naturalist . . . has an easy conscience because he believes that . . . he can easily return to the innocency of nature." [35]

We must keep these points in mind as we note that the naturalist not only expects to find his remedy in the harmonious merging of himself with nature but also assumes that such merging is easy to accomplish. Less superficially, the Idealist tells us the exact opposite. He puts too much trust in the goodness of man which he ascribes without question to the human reason. Man's reason, which is sharply divided from nature, is to guarantee order and control in man, and to protect him against the natural impulses and their unpredictability. A universal mind is postulated, without evidence, and correlated with the human reason. And so the rule of spirit over matter is accepted as certain. The Idealist certainly sees the problem of freedom more clearly than the Naturalist, but he is never capable of seeing the paradox of evil. If he were, he would be forced to admit both the indissoluble unity of spirit and nature in man, and the infection of spirit by sin.

Naturalist and Idealist are both determined not to admit that sin is man's guilt by his own act of will. Niebuhr agrees with Luther's verdict that man's greatest sin is his unwillingness to confess that he is a sinner. That is why secular thinkers try so desperately to banish the permanent problems of the world by a thousand often diametrically opposite solutions. Of course they see that one or many of these solutions (mostly those proposed by others) are false. But they do not see that all of them are insufficient. The truth is that all of them are and remain unworkable when sin is not acknowledged, and man's inability to escape sin and its consequences is not accepted.

"The fact that man can transcend himself in infinite regression and cannot find the end of life except in God is the mark of his creativity and uniqueness; closely related to this capacity is his inclination to transmute his partial and finite self and his partial and finite values into the infinite good. Therein lies his sin." [36]

b. The Source of Human Sin

From the dark wanderings of man's self-excuses and his attempts at self-rescue, as earlier from the clear light of God's original design for man, we have come again to the same point—the point where man's sin lies before us as the mysterious riddle of his rejection of God's loving will for him. But though Niebuhr can speak in one breath of the uniqueness of man and of his sin in a way that reminds us of Pascal's words "the greatness and the misery of man," he is very far from seeking the source of human wrong either in a disturbance of proper proportion in man's nature or in its immaturity. He finds the source incontrovertibly in man's wilful refusal to understand himself, a refusal in which man persists because of his determination to convert his true position of dependence upon God into an absolute, autonomous self-rule. The source of sin, as Niebuhr understands it, is not in what man is but in what he wishes to be.

"It is not the contradiction of finiteness and freedom from which Biblical religion seeks emancipation. It seeks redemption from sin; and the sin from which it seeks redemption is occasioned, though not caused, by this contradiction in which man stands. Sin is not caused by the contradiction because, according to Biblical faith, there is no absolute necessity that man should be betrayed into sin by the ambiguity of his position, as standing in and yet above nature. But it cannot be denied that this is the occasion for his sin.

"Man is insecure and involved in natural contingency; he seeks to overcome his insecurity by a will-to-power which overreaches the limits of human creatureliness. Man is ignorant and involved in the limitations of a finite mind; but he pretends that he is not limited. He assumes that he can gradually transcend finite limitations until his mind becomes identical with universal mind. All of his intellectual and cultural pursuits, therefore, become infected with the sin of pride. Man's pride and will-to-power disturb the harmony of creation. The Bible defines sin in both religious and moral terms. The religious dimension of sin is man's rebellion against God, his effort to usurp the place of God. The moral and social dimension of sin is injustice. The ego which falsely makes itself the centre of existence in its pride and will-to-power inevitably subordinates other life to its will and thus does injustice to other life." [37]

Here we have in a brief but complete statement the core of Niebuhr's thinking. We have reached the centre around which both his brilliant analyses and his attempts to indicate a redemptive solution circle, the nature of sin. All which precedes has this goal; all which follows will clarify the pursuit and attainment. Niebuhr's theology finds its climax and makes its greatest contribution in his doctrine of sin.

Here the relation of human disorder to the two poles, faith and society, comes to full expression. Religious and moral or social differences, like a lens, focus the confusing human questions and human needs, the despairing evasions and resistances of confused man, upon the burning point of human sin. Man's rebellion against God and his enslavement of his fellowmen, lead Niebuhr to a new search for the true position of man. Then sin confronts him as the disorder caused voluntarily by man, which is the exact opposite of the original order of God. God's order set man in communion with God Himself and gave man therefore a freedom unique within all creation. Man desires to usurp for himself the place of God, and by separating himself from his relatedness to God he turns his ordained free position into disorder and slavish dependence upon the powers of this world. The divine order qualified man to love his fellowmen and so to establish true community in society; man, self-willed and self-seeking, breaks the personal tie with his fellowmen, and subjects them, like any inanimate objects, to his insatiable lust for power, which was born from his own insecurity. So he provokes the relentless opposition of other men and brings about his own overthrow and destruction, at the hand of his brothers who have become his enemies. Instead of true community he establishes misdirected and distorted battlelines where every man fights every other, and society ends in total war and anarchy.

To anyone who would exclude himself from the company of the proud and the power-hungry because he is humble and does not desire power and therefore does not consider himself guilty, to him Niebuhr says:

"Sometimes man seeks to solve the problem of the contradiction of finiteness and freedom, not by seeking to hide his finiteness and comprehending the world into himself, but by seeking to hide his freedom and by losing himself in some aspect of the world's vitalities. In that case his sin may be defined as sensuality rather than pride. Sensuality is never the mere expression of natural impulse in man. It always betrays some aspect of his abortive effort to solve the problem of finiteness and freedom. Human passions are always characterized by unlimited and demonic potencies of which animal life is innocent." [38]

So whether the phenomenon of sin be called pride, will-to-power or sensuality, the basic problem is the same. Man, living in tension between finitude and freedom, will not accept the position decreed for him by God, in which the finitude is accepted and the freedom is given meaning and is fulfilled in relatedness. Man is determined to escape finitude by asserting a freedom related not to God but only to himself and therefore falsely related. This determination transforms his freedom into immanent slavery, his true uniqueness into undirected self-love and brings ruin in the individual personality and in society.

Having tried to sketch in broad outline the nature of sin, we now proceed to consider its particular separate beginnings. But this must not be so done as to incur the reproach which we have just given to the secular attempts to explain and solve man's problem, the reproach of secretly excusing sin while apparently merely explaining it. Niebuhr continually says that sin is inevitable but not necessary. Man cannot derive it from a fact of nature and so free himself of responsibility for it. This point, rightly developed, will presently make clearer to us the problem of temptation.

"While the Bible consistently maintains that sin cannot be excused by, or inevitably derived from, any other element in the human situation, it does admit that man was tempted. In the myth of the Fall the temptation arises from the serpent's analysis of the human situation. The serpent depicts God as jealously guarding his prerogatives against the possibility that man might have his eyes opened and become 'as God, knowing good and evil.' Man is tempted, in other words, to break and transcend the limits which God has set for him. The temptation thus lies in his situation of finiteness and freedom. But the situation would not be a temptation of itself, if it were not falsely interpreted by 'the serpent.' The story of the Fall is innocent of a fully developed satanology; yet Christian theology has not been wrong in identifying the serpent with, or regarding it as an instrument or symbol of, the devil. To believe that there is a devil is to believe that there is a principle or force of evil antecedent to any evil human action. Before man fell the devil fell. The devil is, in fact, a fallen angel. His sin and fall consists in his effort to transcend his proper state and to become like God." [39]

According to Niebuhr, that which constitutes sin for men had already happened on a cosmic scale from the same motives and with the same result. Accordingly, when man evades his ordained relatedness to God, he does not face a neutral vacuum. He is captivated by an irresistibly attractive image which not only appears to him to fit his situation exactly and to explain it, but also promises an end of the tension between finiteness and freedom within the compass of man's own powers. Therefore temptation means that man is always in danger of being sucked into the wake of the devil's fall. Outside an unquestioning acceptance of relatedness to God, man finds not a colorless indifference, but the questioning and tempting rebellion of the devil against God.

But the question of the origin of sin is not yet answered. Niebuhr in accordance with the whole Biblical tradition has rightly rejected the more general question "what is the origin of evil?" as falsely stated. Like the Bible, he directs the question to men personally and asks, "How did you come personally and voluntarily to reject the bond to God?" Niebuhr admits a temptation which precedes the human decision; but the decision cannot be derived from the temptation nor be excused by it.

We must sharply distinguish three factors underlying all sin. First, the unique position of man between finiteness and freedom makes sin possible. Man is tied to nature and to the momentariness of his situation in time; but he is also in spirit free to survey not only his own situation but also ways of life other than his own in earlier or contemporary history. Also he is free—specifically made free by the will of God the Creator—to reject the position for which he was created with its access to loving relatedness to God and fellowman which constitutes freedom.

Now comes the second factor, the moment of temptation. The rejection, already made by the devil, is presented to man as a desirable opportunity.

A third and different element is human greed and anxiety, resulting from the two preceding factors when man accepts the devilish proposition of the tempter and determines to establish his own position, contrary to the original order of God. When man has once rejected his relatedness to God, and so loses the shelter of God's support and becomes conscious of his uncertainty and lack of protection; he is misled by his greed for security and support into unlimited anxiety for his own existence.

Much depends on our ability to recognize how Niebuhr's whole understanding of anthropology and theology turns on the pivot of the true comprehension and the correct evaluation of *anxiety* (this anxious greed and greedy anxiety). Niebuhr has no simple and easy definition of sin. Like all Biblically grounded Christian thinkers, he is halted before the mysterious fact of sin. But like other such thinkers, he is not afraid to state explicitly that at bottom all, literally all, even well-intentioned and so-called good human actions not only stand under suspicion of sin, but are in reality sinful.

Sin is never merely doing something badly which one could have done better. No! Sin is a bad, a poisonous, leaven which affects man's whole being and spoils it, inevitably; yet it is not possible to speak of this corruption as a necessity of man's nature. Sin arises at the point where man only in the whole of creation stands, at the point of intersection of nature and spirit where he stands, wretched because his relatedness to God and fellowmen has been lost by his own rejection of it and eager to conquer his own insecurity and transcend the limitations which hamper him. Standing at that intersection, he either exalts himself proudly and tries to create a tyrannical, egocentric order, or he seeks to escape from the tension between finiteness and freedom by surrendering himself to sensuality.

The order of God for man means an inseparable union of nature and spirit, mutually conditioned and fructified, enabled to cohere in relatedness to God. Human sin creates a disorder in which man either sinks into sensuality, relating himself to nature alone, or unsuccessfully seeks to transcend nature, to escape his natural finitude and to free himself in insolent pride from the tension which without communion with God has become unbearable. Without relatedness to God which gives his life meaning and binds him to his fellowmen, man cannot endure. He inevitably destroys himself.

c. Pride and Sensuality as Fruits of Sin

The two signs of sin's corruption, pride and sensuality, must now be more closely examined. It is at once obvious that for

Niebuhr pride produces a much worse disorder in men since it disrupts more ruinously man's true relation to society. Sensuality produces a passive loss of self in slavish mal-adjustment to environment which leaves no place for personal relations because the man himself, having become a thing, degrades all other men to things and so misuses them. But pride leads man to impose his egocentric and enslaving yoke on all around him in his desperate resolve to establish himself as a superman by the exercise of force.

Of course, both sensuality and pride, in similar fashion and for a similar reason, by the exclusion of personal relatedness reduce man's association with his fellowmen to contacts with an impersonal mass. But the objective effects of pride are disproportionately more destructive. The greatness and the misery of man are here closely related. Niebuhr emphasizes the sharp contrast to the original order of God.

"Our present interest is to relate the Biblical and distinctively Christian conception of sin as pride and self-love to the observable behaviour of men. It will be convenient in this analysis to distinguish between three types of pride, which are, however, never completely distinct in actual life: pride of power, pride of knowledge, and pride of virtue. The third type, the pride of self-righteousness, rises to a form of spiritual pride, which is at once a fourth type and yet not a specific form of pride at all but pride and self-glorification in its inclusive and quintessential form." [40]

So Niebuhr disentangles acutely and convincingly the various strands of pride. He has presented them in ascending sequence, the peak of which is spiritual pride culminating in self-deification. He points out that the more unmistakably pride appears in its own form and exhibits its true aim, the more clearly it shows itself to be the wilful repudiation and destruction of man's original position, with its two poles of faith and society. The sin of pride is a usurping rebellion against God, preventing faith and simultaneously producing the intolerant enslavement of men in its most cruel form. Yet it belongs to the nature of sin not to show itself for what it is. Sin seeks to hide itself and to deceive men.

"Our analysis of man's sin of pride and self-love has consistently assumed that an element of deceit is involved in this self-glorification. This dishonesty must be regarded as a concomitant, and not as the basis, of self-love. Man loves himself inordinately. Since his determinate existence does not deserve the devotion lavished upon it, it is obviously necessary to practice some deception in order to justify such excessive devotion.[41]

"The dishonesty which is an inevitable concomitant of sin must be regarded neither as purely ignorance, nor yet as involving a conscious lie in each individual instance. The mechanism of deception is too complicated to fit into the category of either pure ignorance or pure dishonesty." [42]

Dishonesty therefore is characteristic of sin's tactics of confusing by fog and concealment. Sin avoids presenting clear decisions. It does not wish to have the truth about human disorder recognized. It allows man to hide himself modestly from God and man as if such self-concealment were not an evil thing. Such is the way of sin not only in the individual but even more in society. Unusually sharp sight is therefore needed to perceive the sin of collective egoism acutely and distinctly. We are grateful to Reinhold Niebuhr for undertaking to demonstrate that the group not only exhibits a morality which deviates from that of the individual, but also shows more clearly the true nature of sin.

First of all we should learn why he found this difference between the morality of the individual and that of the group.

"This is necessary in part because group pride, though having its source in individual attitudes, actually achieves a certain authority over the individual and results in unconditioned demands by the group upon the individual. Whenever the group develops organs of will, as in the apparatus of the state, it seems to the individual to have become an independent centre of moral life. He will be inclined to bow to its pretensions and to acquiesce in its claims of authority, even when these do not coincide with his moral scruples or inclinations.

"A distinction between group pride and the egotism of individuals is necessary, furthermore, because the pretensions and claims of a collective or social self exceed those of the individual ego. The group is more arrogant, hypocritical, self-centred and more ruthless in the pursuit of its ends than the individual. An inevitable moral tension between individual and group morality is therefore created." [43]

Taught by the events of the last ten years, Niebuhr sees the peak and the peculiar force of group pride in the pride of nations which equate themselves with God.

"The pride of nations consists in the tendency to make unconditioned claims for their conditioned values." [44]

When the limits of just claims are reached and insolently crossed in human pride, human sin is revealed as usurping rebellion against God and at the same time as a destructive disordering of the relations between men. When man's bond to God and fellowmen is broken, this derangement is manifest also at the poles of faith and society.

We have now traced the whole proud up-surge of human attempts at order. Because the original order of God is not recognized *a priori* as essential, these attempts lead only to disorder in all relationships from the almost unknown depths in the consciousness of the individual to the disastrous world-wide disturbances in the international areas of society. We realize that it is no longer possible to find any place for ourselves as contemplative and (more important) as innocent observers outside these events and outside the responsibility for them. No self-exclusion is valid. Nor is there inequality in sin. Sin is not a matter of doing or leaving undone more or less. The decisive test is whether the bond with God is preserved as a living, voluntary, personal relatedness or has been broken.

Niebuhr takes very seriously the belief that sin is a two-fold break which affects first and decisively the relatedness of God and man, and therefore affects no less destructively man's relation to and activity in society. Consistently then he affirms the inequality of guilt as strongly as he insists upon the equality of sin. He would like to muzzle any overzealous theologian who believes that inequality of human guilt must vanish for the greater glory of God, *ad maiorem gloriam dei.*

On the contrary, Niebuhr sees the greatness of God's love for us in His annulling of the break in the relatedness of God and man which is the same for all men personally and individually, and in God's acceptance anew of each one of us, who know ourselves to be guilty, each in his especial way. Therefore Niebuhr will not permit the mediaeval and general Catholic tradition of casuistical treatment of natural law to re-appear. At any price he will preserve personal free will, determining human guilt and divine forgiveness.

"Yet men who are equally sinners in the sight of God need not be equally guilty of a specific act of wrong-doing in which they are involved. It is important to recognize that Biblical religion has emphasized this inequality of guilt just as much as the equality of sin." [45]

The sin of pride imposes upon us a double task. We must not allow ourselves to be deceived by the attempts of men or groups of men who, in order to appear innocent before other men, are desirous of decorating or of hiding their guilt before God by various pretensions and so-called good works. All lack the honor they should have before God.

But on the other hand, we must not fall into a theological Teutonic fury and try to equate or erase all differences of guilt among men, making just judgment impossible. The love of Christ, which brought us forgiveness of our own guilt before God in order that we might forgive our debtors, purposes the renewal and restoration of our relatedness to our fellowmen precisely where it was broken and corrupted. Love does not put all on an equality. It makes possible the personal, unique character of every relation between individuals, because we ourselves after our individual breaking away from God—a break common to us all—have been restored by God, by His personal love to each one of us. We, having become new men, real persons in the true sense of the word, now turn to our fellowman in order to establish with him the same kind of loving personal relatedness. So society may become community. Neither of the two poles of human order, neither faith nor society, may be overlooked in the new life ordered by God's love.

If we have understood the significance of true personality for the renewal of society, and if we know that the loving call of God will create a real person, it is easy for us to see, after brief consideration, that sensuality, the alternative possibility to the sin of pride, offers man no better escape from his confusion. Sensuality hopes to end the tension between finiteness and freedom by voluntarily surrendering man's freedom as a person (that is surrendering man himself), and plunging into finitude, into a state determined by and enveloped in nature. Man hopes thereby to escape all personal and human responsibility.

"A provisional distinction must certainly be made. If selfishness is the destruction of life's harmony by the self's attempt to centre life around itself, sensuality would seem to be the destruction of harmony within the self, by the self's undue identification with and devotion to particular impulses and desires within itself." [46]

"Sensuality is always: (1) an extension of self-love to a point where it defeats its own ends; (2) an effort to escape the prison house of self by finding a god in a process or person outside the self; and (3) finally an effort to escape from the confusion which sin has created into some form of subconscious existence." [47]

d. Sin and Responsibility

Behind all that has been said so far regarding sin as man's voluntary choice of disorder, there remained always the unspoken question of the relation of human sin to human responsibility. This question cannot be evaded by Niebuhr who asserts so strongly the personality and freedom of man in his behavior toward God and his fellowmen. His answer will give the final clarification to our understanding of the essentials of Niebuhr's doctrine of sin.

"Sin is to be regarded as neither a necessity of man's nature nor yet as a pure caprice of his will. It proceeds rather from a defect of the will, for which reason it is not completely deliberate; but since it is the will in which the defect is found and the will presupposes freedom the defect cannot be attributed to a taint in man's nature."[48]

Niebuhr is again confronted with the whole problem of human personality, which we have already met when we were considering man's original state as ordained by God. But the problem now appears in the new context of the human rejection of this original order. This rejection risked and lost the unquestioning union between man and God. It is decisive for the course of Niebuhr's thinking that he does not seek simply for a sort of construction flaw in human nature in order to be able to throw the responsibility for the creature, man, back to the Creator. Nor does he look for an original sin which would in itself be the cause of the false direction taken by the human race who would now be merely following the well-trodden path. When Niebuhr definitely accepts the old theological doctrine of original sin, this acceptance is a part of his effort to discover the essential nature of human sin which underlies every particular sinful action.

If we wish to consider man's responsibility, we must first take up afresh the meaning of temptation. Niebuhr says that temptation pictures man's finiteness as a prison wall ensuring his enslavement to God, and shows its opposite, infinity, in dazzling contrast. Actually such contrast is only quantitative, and the picture is therefore unfair, even false. The true opposite to pure finiteness considered as limitation lies in the qualitative possibility of human life, in obedient assent to the loving will of God. So the words of Jesus are to be understood: "Whosoever loseth his life for my sake shall find it."

Inner communion with God does not mean obliteration of the self but, on the contrary, the fulfillment of the self; for God desires not the death of the sinner, but that he live. The love of God will not extinguish him who receives it, but will raise him to his true station.

Man's acceptance of the tempting summons to rebellion against God betrays therefore the human lack of trust and faith in God's good will towards man. Here is the line between temptation and man's own decision. Here the shifting from faith, one pole of human order, to mistrust of God becomes visible in its significance. At the pole of faith the question of human responsibility is really decided. At the other pole, in man's relation to society, pride and sensuality produce as the result of man's decision, injustice. Even the sin of man points to the polarity of faith and society in their co-ordination and their reciprocal meaning.

Sin therefore can never be derived and explained from temptation alone. The voice of conscience gives man always the knowledge of his responsibility. So we are forced to agree that sin for man is actually inevitable but not deterministically necessary. Self-love, sin's motive power, shows that sin is a voluntary distortion of the destiny of man, from relatedness to absolute autarchy, made by man alone.

Niebuhr's answer then leads to this conclusion: the facts of experience teach us that man in spite of the inevitability of sin has a feeling of responsibility. But one must dig deeper. Already the fact that man can never avow his self-love freely and frankly but must always pretend that he is acting in the universal interest demands further thought. Sin is not the natural consequence of the unique position of man in tension between finiteness and freedom, although it necessarily occurs in that tension. For if man would remain in and naturally and obediently adapt himself to his original position as ordained by God, the tension would remain within its proper limits without driving man to insecurity and greedy anxiety.

Niebuhr agrees here with Kierkegaard, that the only possible answer to the question of origin is that sin causes itself. This throws a significant light on the real content of the doctrine of original sin when it is correctly understood. There can be no general explanation of sin in itself. It can be comprehended by no philosophic interest in its origin. Whatever theories of sin and its origin may be formulated, sin's true nature remains the concern of him only who stands in repentance before the loving God who is his Judge. Regardless of all theories, man himself must confess himself personally as fully responsible for his sin. He must confess that he voluntarily turned away from the life-giving God and from men in need of his brotherliness, that he sought himself only and so lost all, that he now must present himself without defense before God, his Judge.

Sin manifests itself in man in the insecure, greedy anxiety in which he strives to establish and protect himself against God, against nature and against his fellowmen, against danger and destruction. Man in his anxious greed desires eternity, "deep, deep, eternity" as Nietzsche said. But man can receive eternity only in loving and voluntary obedience to the God who is person and who wills man's personal, obedient relatedness to Him. Otherwise eternity changes, in the hands of the man who grasps at it, into the timeless torture of loneliness and insecurity which rends him and drives him to new desperate insanities, to final ruin.

Man enters every Paradise he wins only to find it already spoiled, giving him only the realization of his own loneliness. But total solitude is hell. The loving bond to his fellowmen, since it is not a free mutual gift—and how can it be that when two lost and famished men meet each other?—is transformed into despairing conflict in which each seeks to misuse the other and to secure himself.

Although sin may be as inexplicable as it is inevitable, it remains something for which man is responsible. Man may in his desperate greed undermine by his own power the poles of his true position, faith and society; he may lay violent hands upon them to force them to contribute to his independence, since he believes that he can grasp them and set them up as he pleases. In his hands they lose the life which reaches them only within loving obedient relatedness to God and stiffen to dead objects, to destroyed and destructive monstrosities. Their ruins fall on the rebellious man and prove to him negatively what they were meant, within a secure and living relatedness, to prove positively: it is not good for man to be alone.

Niebuhr emphatically insists, first, that sin cannot be minimized as minor single errors of morality which could be avoided with a little more insight and wisdom. Then the fundamental distortion of man's attitude and action and the weight of his responsibility would be denied. Secondly, he insists that sinful man is not to be defined as a creature hopelessly and absolutely entangled in sin with no possibility of escape and with no real protection against sin so that it could be said "Sin, thy name is man." For then in the opposite way, man's responsibility for sin is made equally impossible.

Niebuhr will never deny either the burden of sin or the freedom of man which is the first condition of responsibility. Against the first error, he cites the convincing objection that since sin exhibits itself most prominently as pride, there can be no intellectual or spiritual summit where man can boast of his achievements and can congratulate himself on having climbed above sin's dangerous flood and left it below him. On the contrary, the higher man thinks he has climbed and the more he believes that he has reason to boast, the more he involves himself in the sin of rebellion against God and of tyranny over his fellowmen. Every higher or more fully developed human possibility offers always correspondingly greater opportunity for sinful yielding to the pride of self-love and therefore for the essence of sin itself. Therefore spiritual pride is the greatest of all sins, presenting itself at the apparently righteous and pious summits of society. "Wherefore let him that thinketh he standeth, take heed lest he fall" (I Cor. 10:12). The opposite error considers man's nature as absolutely and inescapably corrupt and therefore does not rightly judge the true nature of sin.

Sin belongs to the unfathomable mystery of God, who never lets sinful man fall out of His hand nor from the domain of His seeking love. Else the God who is Almighty would not be also absolute love and would not be the only true and just judge. Man's conscience, which so long as it speaks at all testifies that man in his original state decreed by God is truly a person, and accuses him of perversion, is based upon this understanding of sin and proves its correctness. It is man, loved by God, loved in freedom and endowed with will, man at the meeting place of finiteness and freedom, of nature and spirit—it is only this man who can really sin. Sin is the final, almost unbelievable denial by man of the basis of his own existence.

We read between the lines here the experience of a vital and honest man, an experience such as we find in Augustine's *Confessions*. The thinking parallels Luther's statement that by our power much is accomplished, surprisingly much, but not the whole. Just when we desire to do the whole, to complete our great and foolish rejection of our own potentiality as given and ordained by God, we fall helpless and hopeless, in our fall pulling down everything around us.

But Niebuhr does not end with complete negation. Like a hopeful gleam in the dark confusion and ruin of man's disorder falls the word of repentance. Repentance does not aid man to achieve his own self-willed goal but requires that he cease contemplating and evaluating himself in greedy anxiety and that he bow unreservedly and trustfully before God, his Judge, in acceptance of God's true judgment upon him.

We have already indicated that there lies the possibility of restoration, that from the repentant acceptance of God's judgment the new beginning and the restoring of man to his true relatedness with God and his fellowmen can be conceived. The word of repentance, the most impossible possibility for the self-centred man, but given by God to man as a new possibility, brings us to the last section of our investigation.

3. The Restoration of Order to Man

a. The Place of Restoration

In the preceding section we have been forced to admit that man becomes a sinner and falls into confusion by his voluntary rejection of his true position in the original order decreed by

God. This rejection means that man, set by God in tension between finiteness and freedom, is determined to end that tension (which in obedient relatedness to God would be good and meaningful), independently and by his own power. So he either in pride denies his finitude or in sensuality surrenders his freedom. Either way he loses the creative powers which flow to him from inner communion with God and becomes, in the independent isolation which he has chosen, a victim to the powers which he tries to coerce.

If man is to be rescued from the confusion into which he has fallen, we must ask what specific renewal is needed to restore order. The answer must be renewal of his relation to nature and to history, for these two correspond to man's unique position of union in tension between finitude and freedom.

Man is indeed like all the rest of creation a part of nature, but uniquely in creation he is not this only. He surveys, in the transcendence of spirit, his own existence in nature and time and the complex of nature and the course of time so that it becomes to him history. History is human action and experience as known to man. History affords clear demonstration of the results of human disorder. History as seen by man (*sub specie hominis*) is the record of the desperate efforts of men to master the powers of nature and time by their own strength in order to free themselves from human delinquency and guilt. History as seen from eternity (*sub specie aeternitatis*) records the divine revelation of the love of God which in justice and mercy overcomes human disorder. It records God's victory and His verdict.

We have therefore good reason to begin the discussion of the restoration of man with a consideration of history.

"Man's ability to transcend the flux of nature gives him the capacity to make history. Human history is rooted in the natural process but it is something more than either the determined sequences of natural causation or the capricious variations and occurrences of the natural world. It is compounded of natural necessity and human freedom. Man's freedom to transcend the natural flux gives him the possibility of grasping a span of time in his consciousness and thereby of knowing history. It also enables him to change, reorder and transmute the causal sequence of nature and thereby to *make* history. The very ambiguity of the word 'history' (as something that occurs and as something that is remembered and recorded) reveals the common source of both human actions and human knowledge in human freedom." [49]

History therefore is for Niebuhr both fruit and proof of man's freedom. But history is not made by that freedom alone. It is made by the interaction of free man with nature and time and their laws under which he lives. Thus history proves equally the freedom and the creaturehood of man. Like sin, history originates where nature and spirit in man meet, at the point of contact of human freedom and human finitude.

If the history of sinful man must be the record of the development of his rebellion and self-centredness, then the restoration of man must mean that he wins back, in true relatedness to God and fellowmen, his true position between nature and spirit, between finiteness and freedom. The history of restored man will record the results of this renewal. Since history is only possible because of the unique relation of nature and spirit in man, it can never be understood and interpreted from one of the two elements alone, neither from nature nor from spirit.

Thus our understanding of history develops out of our understanding of man, his capacities, potentialities and necessities. The nature of history reflects exactly the problem of man and expands it to include his environment and all of mankind. Not only does history display the peculiar character of humanity; it also poses with utmost insistence the question of society. History never sets up the individual in isolation as an object for observation. It would be entirely unhistorical to fail to relate him to the environment which he influenced and by which he was influenced. Therefore inquiry into the relation of these mutually conditioning elements, into the meaning of their interaction, into their aims and the fulfillment of their aims, cannot be evaded. The consideration of the nature of history entails the question of the interpretation of history.

To explain history as due to the capacity of the human spirit to survey events in time objectively requires in turn the justification of such an explanation and the necessary presuppositions for it. This question arises because man can on the one hand, when he considers history, transcend and survey it, while on the other hand he himself is included in the process of history and is bound by its particularities so that he cannot be wholly objective. This fact is the more important because man himself actively shares in the events. He is summoned, because of his unique position in creation, either himself to give meaning and aim to history or, if this task is beyond his abilities, at least to comprehend an aim which has been set and to act in accordance with it. Interpretation of history without considering meaning and aim is wholly impossible; they can never be separated in man's examination of history.

These questions reduce themselves to one—whether man, capable of only partial self-transcendence, can really interpret history and determine its goal. If it is true that history must be given meaning and its goal must be set from beyond itself, then the question must be answered in the negative. A "yes" would be possible only if there were at man's disposal directions and insights from beyond history which he could never gain either by himself or from history itself.

On the other hand, if history is meaningless, the existence of the individual in history is meaningless. Man in knowing history has already attempted to interpret it. But the decision upon its value or worthlessness falls at the point where man resolves either to interpret history independently and by his own self-will, or to allow the meaning to be disclosed to him from beyond himself and from beyond the historical world. It becomes clear that behind the question of the relation of man to and in history stands the fundamental question of the relation of man to God.

There is then little likelihood that any wholly immanent explanation of history can encompass the meaning of history. If we review the varying interpretations of history which have been offered through the centuries, we find that they can be classified as follows:

"Western culture embodies three approaches toward the vexing problem of the nature of human history: 1. The approach of Greek classicism which equated history with the world of nature and sought emancipation of man's changeless reason from this world of change; 2. the Biblical-Christian approach which found man's historic existence both meaningful and mysterious and which regarded the freedom of man, which distinguished history from nature, as the source of evil as well as of good; and the modern approach which regarded the historical development of man's power and freedom as the solution for every human perplexity and as the way of emancipation from every human evil."[50]

It is easy to see that Greek antiquity ultimately rejected the idea of meaningfulness in history. Nor can the modern view present any meaning which corresponds with reality, for the modern secular view takes no account of the essential nature of man or of his sinful distortion of that nature with its results in history. Although the modern view is closer to the truth that history has meaning, it breaks down because it lacks a true understanding of man. It does not see (what the preceding investigation has established) that man, wholly self-dependent, man apart from relatedness to God who transcends the world, is incapable of giving meaning to his own life and to history.

Hence it becomes clear that man's sinful disorder not only involves his own individual existence and the existence of all mankind, but that it also so permeates history as the sphere of human action that it is not possible for man, confused by sin, to perceive the God-given meaning of history nor to make it actual. On the contrary, man's sin misleads him into imposing on history his own self-willed aim of self-glorification. History's goal is entirely distorted and is set up in the wrong direction.

Niebuhr therefore maintains firmly that without faith man's

historical existence can have no meaning. He then draws the conclusion that a faith which fails to give such meaning cannot be called true faith. True faith, he believes, binds man to the God who so values man that He seeks him within history and takes upon Himself man's historical living. God's loving relatedness to man is the basis of the meaning of history. Without it, history remains meaningless.

b. The Nature of the Restoration of Man

Since man by himself cannot know the true meaning of history, dependent as that meaning is upon the position which God ordained for man, but transforms it into its opposite by his sinful self-will, the aid to his restoration must be twofold: the revelation of the true meaning of history and the transformation of man, distorted by sin, into an obedient, God-related bearer and fulfiller of the divine meaning in and for history. These two aspects of God's restoration of man Niebuhr finds in Old Testament prophecy and in the Old Testament expectation of a Messiah.

Prophecy reveals especially that God in His love does not leave man alone to continue in his sinful confusion; He makes known to him again and again His will and His purpose for the individual and for all mankind, through His word proclaimed by the prophets. By the prophetic word, God restores the individual to true community within the nation and gives him a definite task in the whole community of the nations of the world. God reveals through the prophets that He has an all-inclusive purpose of redemption in and for all world history and that He commands man to work towards the fulfillment of this purpose in true *social action.*

But by this revelation of the will of God, man's powerlessness, indeed his complete perversion by sin, is disclosed. Not merely is man incapable of the task set him and in need of constant inner relatedness to God; man is also unwilling to accept either the task or the relatedness.

The hope for a divine helper, the expectation of a Messiah, confirms the fact of human incapacity, and the human desires embodied in the formulation of the Messianic hope show equally that what is desired by man is only his own self-centred satisfaction, his self-justification in his own security. He does not desire his obedient inclusion in the fulfillment of God's will in and for history. Therefore God's revelation of the true Messiah always sharply contradicts the Messianic expectation of men.

Jesus of Nazareth, who is the Christ of God's revelation, does not correspond to man's expectation of a Messiah, and He is therefore crucified by men as a blasphemer against God. With Jesus, history attains its goal for all men; from Him that goal receives today new, effectual and complete meaning. By Him man is judged, and by Him the spirits are judged. In Him history is revealed and fulfilled. He is the foundation stone, the essence and the fulfillment of man's existence. He is Himself the new man for us and in us, the second Adam and *Christus in nobis*.

For Niebuhr theology and the interpretation of history are closely inter-related, and for both the Christ event is central. He will not interpret either without reference to the other, nor attempt to comprehend either in isolation from the other. But just as little would he confuse them. They are closely bound together, but they do not encroach upon each other. Gospel and world are related to each other, without at all losing their wholly distinct character. They persist in close relationship, but it is an active relationship and determinative to the highest degree. It is God's revelation in prophecy and the Messianic hope which encounters history directly and judges it, which uncovers and judges the false goals and vain wishes of men. Because history is the bearer of God's redeeming activity moving towards its goal, and also at the same time the bearer of man's sinful self-will and rebellion, intolerable tension exists between the redemptive will of God and the sinful will of man, between grace and sin. God's purpose and man's hopes are wholly incongruous.

"The fact that there can be no Christ without an expectation of Christ relates Christianity as founded in a unique revelation to the whole history of culture; the fact that the true Christ cannot be the Messiah who is expected separates Christianity from the history of culture." [51]

Such is Niebuhr's view of the relation of revelation and history. Revelation answers a human need which is expressed throughout the history of cultures. But it so answers it that the true Christ absolutely denies man's false and self-centred Messianic hopes. Only to man in true relatedness to Himself does God in Christ reveal Himself as He is, as the God who in His redeeming love claims man for Himself in order that man may carry that love with its restoring power into society and so be directed toward the goal at the end of the days. Man can know and acknowledge this revelation only in true relatedness to God. Only in that relatedness can man comprehend the true meaning of his own existence and of all history.

So we are again confronted by the fact of sin. Sin underlies man's rejection and rebellion, and sin necessitates man's restoration by God. It shows itself in the manifest incapacity of man to restore himself to the true relatedness to God which alone would make possible for him the attainment of his true position in nature and history and so enable him to gain the true relation to his fellowmen.

The false Messianic hopes of men show that man vouchsafes only sinful rejection to one pole of the order decreed by God, to faith. Even when man expects a Messiah, he expects wrongly. A Christ has indeed been expected, but this expectation could not in its self-centredness look towards the restoration of man by God in Jesus Christ. Who and of what sort is the Christ sent by God, and how He can combine God's justice and love, His wrath and His grace—all that remains extraneous to man's hope.

Clearly, the question of particular or historical (Niebuhr calls it with especial emphasis *historical*) revelation is here raised. It is important to Niebuhr that history be recognized as the area where the peculiar uniqueness of man is most plainly seen. In that area is manifested how nature and time provide the human possibility by virtue of which the simple sequence of events becomes history, actions shaped and experienced by men, remembered and reported by them.

But here also is revealed man's total confusion, what Schiller meant when he said "Welt Geschichte Welt Gericht," the history of the world condemns the world. However, the idealist's striking phrase is actually untrue, since history can judge itself no more than it can fulfil itself. World judgment and world fulfillment come from the transcendent God who acts in and for history. We who know the act of God as it affects an individual man, may speak of restoration of man to his original true state. But when its world wide significance for the existence of all mankind and their destiny is recognized, God's redeeming act must be called historical or special revelation in Jesus Christ.

Here we should remind ourselves of what has been previously said concerning the general revelation of God in the creation and in the personal experience of individuals, for Niebuhr builds his conception of the special historical revelation in Jesus Christ on this foundation. Belief in the transcendent God, the Creator, entails the acknowledgement of responsibility before this God for the life given by Him; God is recognized as Judge. But through the continuing prophetic word and through the full revelation in Jesus Christ, God is revealed as both Judge and Redeemer of the lives of men. The Old Testament covenant relation between the people of God and their Lord crystalized the general feeling of moral obligation into a definite, mutual, and personal bond defined by the commandments and man's fulfillment of them.

Because man by his sinful self-will proved himself incapable and undesirous of this mutual bond, and so incurred the guilt of transgressing and breaking it, the prophetic message had always to stress that the sin of man's proud and fruitless rejection of God lies under the condemnation of God. Sin in the eyes of the prophets is man's unwillingness to acknowledge himself a creature, dependent upon God, and man's effort to make his own life independent and secure. Sin is the "vain imagination" by which man seeks to conceal the contingent, accidental, and dependent nature of his own existence and to give it the appearance of unconditioned, divine reality.

So the message of revelation through the Old Testament prophets, in which God Himself spoke to man in his confusion, corresponds exactly to what we have tried to present in the preceding sections. Our starting point was the general problem of man and the disorder into which he has fallen. We were then forced to recognize that the disorder of the sin of breaking the relatedness to God and fellowmen is central and causal. The word of the Lord came to the prophets and commanded them to uncover sin in its finest ramifications, in its craftiest concealments, because the God of the Covenant is the loving God who wills to restore His people again to the bond of loving obedience. In drastic contrast to the light of God's constant faithfulness, man's sin of stiff-necked refusal and self-will shows doubly black and incomprehensible.

Furthermore, the prophet interpreted the events of history and saw in them the results of human sin which called forth God's just anger and condemnation. Yet this judgment is not mere destruction; it purposes to recall man from his wrong course.

"The catastrophes of history by which God punishes this pride, it must be observed, are the natural and inevitable consequences of men's effort to transcend their mortal and insecure existence and to establish a security to which man has no right. One aspect of this human pride is man's refusal to acknowledge the dependent character of his life." [52]

The New Testament, when it speaks of sin, accepts the prophetic verdict; and the New Testament understanding of sin, although sharpened and clarified, is essentially the same as the prophetic.

"The most classical definition of sin in the New Testament, that of St. Paul [in Romans 1:18–23], is conceived in terms of perfect consistency with this prophetic interpretation. The sin of man is that he seeks to make himself God." [53]

The Biblical teaching of the Old and New Testaments, then, is at one in the understanding of sin and therefore also at one in the standpoint from which history is judged.

"The serious view which the Bible takes of this sin of man's rebellion against God naturally leads to an interpretation of history in which judgment upon sin becomes the first category of interpretation. The most obvious meaning of history is that every nation, culture and civilization brings destruction upon itself by exceeding the bounds of creatureliness which God has set upon all human enterprises." [54]

Here only one side of the Biblical revelation of the restoration of man, the negative side, the exposure of man's disorder is stressed. Here both the significance and the limitation of the Old Testament is shown. Although the Old Testament includes prophetic pronouncements which point to a divine rescue, on the whole the negative prevails. This does not mean that the Old Testament is of less value—still less that it is superfluous—because the New Testament presents all which is most important. The church always has protested against any such assumption. On the contrary, Old and New Testament constitute together a closely bound, mutually dependent whole of promise and fulfillment. But it is also important to see that neither Testament is identical with the other even though neither excludes the other and that they stand in a reciprocally definitive relation.

The Old Testament leaves us with an unanswered question. But it is exactly this question and no other which is taken up and answered in the New Testament. What the Old Testament prophets hesitantly suggest and what the writers of the Messianic apocalypses in post-exilic Judaism could not comprehend, was the union of judge and redeemer in the One God, Jehovah. This question found its solution in the saving act of God in Jesus Christ, according to the "good news" of the New Testament.

God as Judge considered man's guilt heavy. He did not blur the difference between good and evil. He did not declare a general amnesty which would leave guilt unexpiated. Yet God loves man and "wills not the death of the sinner," but rather that he repent. He sees man's heart and knows that sin is not merely the regrettable slip of an essentially good man, but a perversion of the will which deforms the whole man and distorts all his thoughts and deeds.

God then takes upon Himself the guilt of sin and all its fatal consequences, in the atoning death of His Son on Golgotha. By His personal giving of Himself in the Holy Spirit to each individual man, He gives to men this redemption, so that every man becomes a new creature in inner communion with God.

The "new" in the historical revelation in Jesus Christ, the "special" in contrast to the general revelation, is that God who is strictly and wholly Judge is not that only; that He is also the Saviour of men; that in God love overcomes wrath by giving it full satisfaction. The essence of God and the nature of God are this love, and this love victoriously wipes out the sin which apparently separates man from God. Yet the freedom of personality which carries the heavy burden of the results of sin is not annulled. The love of God wins man without coercing him.

The total act of love brings man again to his unique position where, in the free response of love, he can accept the offered communion with God which enables him to find again a renewed bond of love to his fellowmen. Therefore Jesus Christ is the final and full revelation of God, to be superseded by no other, and to be continued only in the work of the Holy Spirit.

It is significant that when the content of historical or special revelation of God has been defined as the revelation of Christ and in Christ, a discrimination between it and general revelation at once follows. Still more significant is the way in which Niebuhr sees the distinction. In contrast to the general theological usage which insists on a sharp and immutable separation in order to protect one kind of revelation from the dominance of the other, Niebuhr, although fully recognizing the difference, can see a close and pregnant connection between them. For him, historical revelation does not begin from the opposite end and run its whole course counter to general revelation. Rather it follows, pursuing the same direction, in order to change a vaguely felt experience and hope into the certainty which only historical revelation can give.

If we now ask what especial basis Niebuhr has for the view

which he urges, we find it in his conviction that the whole revealing activity of God is one and indivisible. This unity depends on the nature and activity of God as constant self-giving love to men and to human society as a whole.

Man's sinful disorder required a special, historical revelation of God, a revelation experienced by men as something different from general revelation. Yet revelation, not in the sight of men, *sub specie hominis*, but in the sight of God, *sub specie aeternitatis*, must be so understood that not man's recognition of the difference which his sin makes necessary, but the love of God, is definitive.

Niebuhr therefore can admit no real discontinuity between general and special revelation. The question is decided not by man's knowledge but by the fact that the act of God has made possible and actual a new and real communion between God and man, because man has been newly restored to his proper position in relatedness to God and society.

c. The Effect of the Restoration of Man

It is wholly in line with Niebuhr's thinking and method of procedure that he now turns directly to the consideration of the effects of the restoration of man by God's redeeming act in Jesus Christ. Whatever he thought characteristic of the original state of man as ordained by God, whatever seemed to him to have been distorted or destroyed by man's sinful disorder, all that must now be made new if man's restoration is achieved. Man again in communion with God is enabled to form a new community in society and to serve in bringing its fulfillment.

Niebuhr then traces the growth of community from the beginning of Christianity, finding the measure of the restoration of men as they accepted or rejected the specific revelation in Jesus Christ to be their relatedness in community. Whatever through the restoration of man to relatedness with God and society became new or different, what took form and persisted, made possible a fuller comprehension of the nature of the restoration.

"The Christian community came into being by the faith that Jesus was the Christ who had fulfilled the expectations of the ages. But this belief runs counter to the actual expectations of the prophetic movement in the period of its culmination. The Christ whom Christian faith accepts is the same Christ whom Messianism rejects, as not conforming to its expectations. The acceptance would not have been possible if Jesus had not himself transformed the Messianic expectation in the process of negating and fulfilling it." [55]

The return of man to his original state must begin first of all with the destruction of the false hopes and systems of his sinful confusion. These stand in the way of the true justification of the repentant sinner by God, for man has misused even religion to justify himself against God.

Jesus rejected Hebrew legalism as "a kind of arrested and atrophied religion of history." For this rejection Niebuhr sees three reasons: 1. "No law can do justice to the freedom of man in history." 2. "No law can do justice to the complexities of motive which express themselves in the labyrinthine depths of man's interior life." 3. "Law cannot restrain evil; for the freedom of man is such that he can make keeping the law the instrument of evil." [56]

But Jesus also rejects nationalistic particularism; and finally He rejects the answer of Hebrew Messianism to the problem set by the prophets, for

"This ultimate problem is given by the fact that human history stands in contradiction to the divine will at any level of its moral and religious achievements in such a way that in any 'final' judgment the righteous are proved not to be righteous. The final enigma of history is therefore not how the righteous will gain victory over the unrighteous, but how the evil in every good and the unrighteousness of the righteous is to be overcome." [57]

This standard of judgment, a standard reversing all others and therefore the only truly revolutionary standard, was proclaimed by Jesus, put in practice by Him, and validated by Him; but it will become fully clear only in the judgment upon the world at the end of the days. This standard makes it incontrovertible that with Jesus Christ something new, which before did not exist in the heart of man, invaded the world.

Because Niebuhr sees here the decisive content of the message of Jesus, he gives eschatology a central place in his theology. Moreover, he looks at history from the eschatological view-point, and judges from that view-point man's attempts at interpretation and solution, even man's theories of religion. Rightly Niebuhr rejects any premature closing by man of the gap between the first and second coming of Christ to earth. Every such attempt falsifies the position of man, stationed by God, in history, between the revelation of history's meaning and its fulfillment; even as he is stationed between finiteness and freedom.

Jesus Himself combatted the prophetic commingling of revelation of the kingdom of God and its accomplishment. He devoted His first coming to the task of the suffering servant. His second coming is to reveal the rule of the triumphant Son. On the one side, the high point of history for Niebuhr is the disclosure of the hidden sovereignty of God; on the other side, history is still awaiting its high point in the second coming of the triumphant Messiah.

Hence Niebuhr draws his significant conclusion that present history is an "Interim" between the first and second coming of Christ, between the revelation of the meaning of history and its fulfillment. This must be so, since sin is overcome in principle but not in fact, and love must be constant in suffering instead of triumphant. In such a Christian interpretation of history, both the pessimism of asceticism and world denial is overcome, and the modern unfounded optimism of world bliss is avoided. The Christian is saved, but saved in hope. Death which always threatens life with meaninglessness is swallowed up in victory, but death still remains at the end of every life. Both the immanence and the transcendence of life are preserved and keep their allotted meaning. To understand life and history according to the meaning which Christ has given them means to be able to endure the chaos of any present, and the danger of any future without sinking into despair.

The "Interim" which Niebuhr considers essential for understanding the position of man in history and for its interpretation is very different from the concept of Schweitzer when he speaks of an "Interim Ethic." Schweitzer believes that the whole New Testament attitude to the world and history, especially the view of Paul, depended on the conviction that a very short and in itself insignificant period of time would intervene between the life of Jesus and the Parousia. When the time was prolonged, the New Testament view ceased to be relevant. Niebuhr accepts the "Interim" idea, but this "Interim" can continue indefinitely, since for him the date of the second coming is not important. The essential is the reality and meaning of Christ's second coming which must be so understood that we find ourselves always in the tension between the revelation of the meaning of life and history in the first coming of Christ and its fulfillment in His return.

Here as always it is necessary to understand the Word of the Bible rightly if we would know how to accept its message in real obedience. The Word is not to be taken in verbal literalness, but acceptance of its meaning and purpose creates a living relatedness between God and man. Niebuhr rightly sees in the literalist and fundamentalist misapprehension the very mistake which ought especially to be avoided. Man degrades God's personal and voluntary Word to man, the Word which demands from man personal and voluntary obedience, into an impersonal, neuter code of behavior which man can hold as a possession of his own, if he is properly taught. Niebuhr insists on the exact opposite. Man, certain of the final judgment which is beyond his grasp and beyond his power to conceive, stands at every moment of his life in the presence of God; and only when the bond to God is restored can he face, understand and endure the vicissitudes of history and death itself. Thus the historical "interim" between the earthly life of Jesus Christ and His final judgment makes us cognizant of the meaning and necessity of man's restoration to his true place in nature and history in relatedness to God and his fellowmen, in the polarity of faith and society.

It is the message of the historical revelation in Christ which illuminates history and our relatedness to it. But because there must be a responsive voluntary and personal turning to God when the redeeming Word of the love of God in Christ asks for man's obedient and loving answer, we must now examine this answer which is the acceptance in faith of this Messiah who was expected —and rejected.

What does Niebuhr really mean by the *faith* which he calls the corollary to revelation and which he says constitutes one pole of human order? He connects it closely on the one side with revelation, for he says that revelation is not completed without faith, and that faith is not possible without revelation. Revelation has absolute precedence, but it attains its end in man's believing response to its word. On the other side, faith offers the human response to God, in which man voluntarily accepts and affirms his relatedness to God. But man's faith is not an independent achievement, some kind of intellectual conclusion which man has reached. Man's conscience bears him witness that faith is the result of the inner inseverable relatedness between God and man. In this communion and in this alone faith recognizes the nature of God's redeeming act.

Faith is much more than contemplation. The dynamic love of God crosses the bridge of revelation and faith, acts on men, and seeks through them to reach and act on other men. Of necessity, then, the love of God continuously gives to the believer a living and meaningful sense of the nature of God and of God's saving act which makes man a new creature. Man by faith experiences in the suffering of Christ the truth, valid for him personally, that the suffering of God is on the one side the necessary consequence of the sinful rejection of good by man, and on the other side the voluntary acceptance of the consequence of sin by God's love.

Therefore faith does not present to the believer in revelation some previously concealed trait of God, nor does it disclose any activity of God which does not have direct meaning for the man himself in his own life—and indeed for every man in the world with his own particular nature and his own problems. There is no area in man or in the world which is untouched by this act of God in behalf of men.

To speak of the power or the righteousness of God is to speak of the true nature of power and of true righteousness, by which man's use of power and man's claim to righteousness are judged. Briefly we can say that God's love is, for Niebuhr, the law of life, apart from which there can be nothing really existent.

Niebuhr now seeks to discover step by step in what relation to each other power and righteousness stand with God, and what connection the two have with God's love and mercy. He can then determine the application of these concepts to the every day world and their concrete exemplification within it. The resulting conclusions unquestionably belong to the most significant of Niebuhr's contributions toward a Christian understanding of our present situation.

Niebuhr does not limit this investigation to the individual believer, for it belongs to the nature of the divine love which restores man, that it restores him immediately to true relatedness to his fellowmen in society. In society, the possibilities and limits of history are first rightly seen, and there the restoration can plainly show itself; just as formerly the sinful disorder manifested itself in its greatest extent in the conflict of men in society.

The effects of the renewing of the individual through his restoration to his true position in society are not classified by Niebuhr into separate ways of behavior or norms. He puts them all explicitly under one heading "the second Adam." Any further elaboration he may make is only a paraphrase of the one theme found in Galatians 2:20, "I am crucified with Christ: Nevertheless, I live; yet not I, but Christ liveth in me." Niebuhr dared in spite of the offense which he gives in wide circles and especially among American theologians and philosophers, to label all his discoveries in Christian ethics with this word from the missionary situation of the first century. His choice illustrates most beautifully and forcibly the truth of what we have already said. The theme of all Niebuhr's thinking is the inner and inseparable relatedness between God and man in the fellowship of society.

Niebuhr proceeds to the careful consideration of the possibilities and the limits of human life and of all history. He examines them as actualities, as they appear to the observer; but he investigates them in the light of the conviction that they are directed toward the fulfillment of God's will to save and have meaning only in relation to that will. He insists that our present existence, our *hic et nunc*, is ordered and must be understood according to the Christian message in order that our attitude and actions may be directed toward the final victory of God at the end of the days. The Christian revelation is not only a revelation of God who is, but also of Him who in Christ tore down the separating wall of sin with all its terrible consequences. And the Christian gospel knows of no other possibility of existence for the new man except that which the same God in Christ, as the Second Adam, created as our new possibility of existence. In that possibility, personal individuality is not lost; on the contrary, the real person has first found himself as the continuing new creative work of Christ in us, *Christus in nobis*.

In these three words is summed up all that has been said of the nature and effect of God's restoration of man.

d. The Goal of Human Restoration

In what follows, we intend to survey the goal of human restoration, and we shall need to understand that goal in a twofold sense. The aim toward which man strives is, we must recognize, both a goal immanent in history and a transcendent goal beyond history. The transcendent goal both determines and makes possible the immanent. The two cannot be separated, but stand in essential relation. The immanent goal, made possible and defined by the transcendent, continually directs the life of individuals and of society so that it looks toward the transcendent goal and moves consciously in the direction fixed by the transcendent. The transcendent goal regulates, encloses and fulfils human life, individually and collectively at the end of the days.

The immanent goal of human restoration is the fulfilling of the will of God by men in the community of society. The transcendent goal, which is at the same time the end of man's temporal life, of society and of history, is set by the final judgment of God on the last day.

a) The Immanent Goal of Human Restoration

Niebuhr, as we learned earlier, sees the new life of man under the Lordship of Christ and actualized by the Second Adam, as restored to true relatedness with God and fellowmen. But he cannot, nor does he desire to, lay down casuistical laws for that relatedness. No more than did St. Paul writing to his first mission churches, does Niebuhr attempt anything of the sort.

On the contrary, he finds the distinguishing mark of this new life to be man's full knowledge that no part of the new power, flowing to him from God's love to make his restoration and his new aim possible, is his own possession. He can use none of it independently and arbitrarily for his own selfish purposes. Any such presumption is exactly the sin which must be overcome and repudiated. Man's new life consists in his full repatriation in God's plan of salvation and therefore his own participation in God's will towards his fellowmen; he now seeks and works for that only.

The Biblical word that we must have as though we had not, because in reality we have nothing which we have not received (cf. I Cor. 4:7); that therefore what we have in faith is ours only so far as through us it may become effective in the world—this is for Niebuhr the true basis of human relatedness. By it man is bound to perpetual humility, by it he is constantly called to repentance, called to recognize his selfish anxiety, his greedy concern for his own life and possessions, his distrust of God in his persistent care for the preservation of his own existence.

If we should now ask Niebuhr why he fixes on just this knowledge as the distinguishing mark of the Christian man, he would reply, because precisely there the paradox (as he calls it) of grace is made manifest. The grace of God which redeems us, delivers us and restores us to our new life cannot for two reasons be *our* possession. First, we could not possibly earn it by our own behavior and services; it is the free gift of God. Second, grace does not hand over something which man can "have" in a literal sense as a possession. What grace gives is a relatedness, man's new bond with God through and in love of Him. Grace also is manifest in the presence of the Holy Spirit which guides and directs our present life and is also the pledge and the promise of our complete eternal communion with God. Grace is, so to say, an eschatological gift, not a possession of which we can boast or to which we could lay claim. Niebuhr has seen the paradox of grace: the more clearly we know that we cannot "have" grace, so much the more do we have it.

Niebuhr now relates this basic knowledge to man's endeavor to attain two goals—truth and justice. He does not condemn all human activity because it is always endangered by self-willed distortion through human sin. He desires only that this danger be recognized in repentance and humility in order that a false confidence in human activity and its possibilities be precluded and human action be subordinated to the power of God's will and to the goal determined by Him. Man's whole duty is to devote himself absolutely to the task appointed for him, and to work with all his might at doing the will of God.

Since the world with all its achievements—most of all with its highest and proudest—stands under the judgment of God in and at the end of history, we cannot be subject to the desire to eternalize or deify ourselves by our achievements. But we are required as obedient servants to offer ourselves unreservedly, in the name of the unlimited love of God and commissioned by that love, for the service of the imperilled world.

In man's search for truth, the especial danger, as Niebuhr sees it, is that man may convince himself that he is in possession of truth. In refutation of any such claim, Niebuhr asserts the truth in Christ, which in a double sense is a truth "above" men. It is pronounced upon him from "Beyond"—that is from God's design for man. This truth above man affirms his bond in freedom to God and his fellowmen. This truth will give to man the true relation between himself and all that is; will give him his true position in the cosmos where, designated from his creation ruler over all created things, he rightly subordinates them to himself, but where at the same time he knows himself bound in loving obedience to the Creator, Preserver and Finisher of all creation.

The test of whether the "truth in Christ," which is truth under the paradox of grace, has been accepted is according to Niebuhr tolerance. Whether and how tolerance is practiced shows whether men recognize that there is an absolute and unlimited truth over men, the truth in Christ, which prohibits the desire to establish *our* truths and insights as final and absolute. This test of tolerance Niebuhr applies to the "various versions" of the Christian faith and to non-Christian philosophies with the following conclusion:

"However we twist or turn, whatever instruments or pretensions we use, it is not possible to establish the claim that we have the truth. The truth remains subject to the paradox of grace. . . . And we will have it the more purely in fact if we know that we have it only in principle. Our toleration of truths opposed to those which we confess is an expression of the spirit of forgiveness in the realm of culture. Like all forgiveness, it is possible only if we are not too sure of our own virtue.

"Loyalty to the truth requires confidence in the possibility of its attainment; toleration of others requires broken confidence in the finality of our own truth. But if there is no answer for a problem to which we do not have the answer, our shattered confidence generates either defeat (which in the field of culture would be scepticism); or an even greater measure of pretension, meant to hide our perplexities behind our certainties (which in the field of culture is fanaticism)." [58]

The necessity for tolerance leads us to the discussion of justice. As a young pastor Niebuhr had seen the injustice behind the mask of a so-called "fair wage" in industrial capitalism. He had experienced the injustice which, by ignoring the man in the worker, robbed men of their humanity. As a result he at first gave his allegiance to radical socialism—not simply because it claimed to exemplify the casuistical *suum quique* of natural law, but because it promised to set us right with our fellowman in a loving personal relation in which he can also give himself to us in free personal agreement.

Because justice in human relationships (from those of individuals to those involving the totality of society) can be attained only through love, the love originating in relatedness to God, the question of justice was for Niebuhr peculiarly urgent. At the pole, society, justice—understood as the consequence of the restoration of man to his place in the arch of relatedness of God and society—must manifest itself or the whole Christian message has lost for Niebuhr its value and its meaning. With genuine prophetic fire, he seeks in society the fruits by which we are to know Christian men as children of God. He insists primarily on the value and the validity of the concept of justice. The kingdom of God is foreshadowed in the struggle for justice. The problem of truth and the conflicts relating to it remain within the frame of the rational and the intellectual. The question of justice penetrates deeply into the very life of men and of society as a whole.

The so-called struggle for survival and insistence on justice stand in a paradoxical relation to each other. Superficially, the one seems to exclude the other; but actually, without the restraint of justice, the survival of man is seriously endangered. It is human sin which, because of its social effects, makes necessary justice in the legal, economic and social sense. Such a justice is a matter of blocking the sinful and hence unjust incursions of one human being into the sphere of life of another. But this blockade cannot remove the cause of the struggle for survival with all its ugly offshoots. The blockade itself is often enough misused as an hypocritical disguise to gain a selfish advantage.

True justice can be grounded neither in the actual necessity for it nor in itself. The foundation for it can be found only in the supporting love of God which permits man, restored to his right position, to see in his fellowman his beloved brother. Then he can desire that this brother also with all that belongs to him may attain his right. Then the struggle for survival, which is really a struggle not for survival but for self-sufficiency, can be wholly abandoned. Instead of every man's hand raised against his neighbor, there will be a community of mutual help.

The paradox of grace means, in the context of justice, that the "begraced" sinner need no longer himself try to justify his existence, need no longer be anxious about himself and greedily seek his own aggrandizement in order to win for himself security and glory. He knows that he is truly alive in the love of God which guards and preserves him; he can actually cast his cares on the Lord, for it is not he who lives but Christ in him and he for Christ. Because this is the foundation, the reality and the fulfillment of his life, he cannot begin or carry out anything against other men, or anything which would profit only himself without benefit to his fellowmen, his brothers.

Yet even here, Niebuhr does not abandon reality for a sentimental vision. He knows that neither the fulfillment nor even the vision of justice is our achievement or within our possibilities. Justice is rather a perpetual judgment ever pronounced anew upon our sin as injury to our fellowmen.

The paradox of grace means here that the more we hunger and thirst after justice and righteousness (rightly understood), the more we ourselves, faced with the infinite love of God, suffer from our own unrighteousness, so much the more shall we be filled. The end of all human life and history will be at the same time the blotting out of sin at the end of the days. Niebuhr sees in justice an eschatological gift which already here and now makes it possible for us humbly and penitently to hope for its fulfillment—not through us, but through God Himself. It is a gift which by its very nature must make us sensitive to every kind of injustice in human society, so that here and now a gleam from the divine justice falls upon the society of men and summons it to community through man's restoration.

Niebuhr therefore rejects the idea that justice is attainable through a fuller development of human reason and rationality. The pursuit of justice requires a union of vitality and reason, because social relations are never purely rational. It demands the harmonious, co-ordinated action of all man's powers of emotion and will as well as of reason. But man by himself never achieves this unification which can only be attained by man guided by God. The love of God makes man a unity and so unites him with his fellowmen that his contemporary becomes his brother.

The love of God is therefore for Niebuhr the fulfillment and the denial of all man's attempts to achieve justice in history. God's love fulfils them as it continually turns men to new and personal relations with their fellowmen as brothers. God's love alone can justify the striving for justice in temporal human existence. But it annuls man's attempts at justice since it shows that they are never in themselves satisfactory or valid. Love sets them perpetually under the judgment of God, who is full, infinite love, who gives Himself as a sacrifice for us. Love nullifies the claim of human achievements when they arrogate to themselves a final significance; it fulfils them when it takes them out of the hands of an always "unprofitable servant" and fulfils them in itself.

Niebuhr, who has always shown an especial aptitude for sociology and political economy and has used it frequently in defense of positions which he has taken publicly, can meet the problems of man in society candidly and simply, just for the reason that he does not expect salvation by human "power-organizations," but by God's restoration of men in the community of society so that the individual man feels his own responsibility within the community.

Niebuhr avoids both of the dangers of religion: flight from the world and involvement in it. The reason for his immunity is clear. He affirms the bond to God which the paradox of grace, in restoring men, extends to all human relationships in the world. He knows that the same judgment which penalizes our sinful ambitions in the social and political organizations of society will judge us all equally and individually. That judgment will determine whether we have taken seriously our loving responsibility for our fellowmen in society; how far the effect of our bond to God is manifest in action, in our struggle to establish, so far as our human situation allows, that justice which is the common need of all men.

This unassuming but consciously responsible position of Niebuhr toward social and political problems appears plainly in his concluding statement of the Christian relation to government—always a dilemma for Protestant theologians.

"Whatever may be the source of our insights into the problems of the political order, it is important both to recognize the higher possibilities of justice in every historic situation, and to know that the twin perils of tyranny and anarchy can never be completely overcome in any political achievement. These perils are expressions of the sinful elements of conflict and dominion, standing in contradiction to the ideal of brotherhood on every level of communal organization. There is no possibility of making history completely safe against either occasional conflicts of vital interests (war) or against the misuse of the power which is intended to prevent such conflicts of interest (tyranny). To understand this is to labor for higher justice in terms of the experience of justification by faith. Justification by faith in the realm of justice means that we will not regard the pressures and counter pressures, the tensions, the overt and the covert conflicts by which justice is achieved and maintained, as normative in the absolute sense; but neither will we ease our conscience by seeking to escape from involvement in them. We will know that we cannot purge ourselves of the sin and guilt in which we are involved by the moral ambiguities of politics without also disavowing responsibility for the creative possibilities of justice."[59]

The restored bond with God gives man a new knowledge of his possibilities but also a new recognition of the limits and the dangers of the voluntary and personal obligation of redeemed men in a society in which God wills to be glorified in a restored community. From this knowledge, Niebuhr wins dynamic freedom for all the new facets and possibilities of society in our time, without believing that we are about to build the kingdom of God here and now. He sees that through the technical advance of our civilization the political problem has become a world problem involving the interdependence of all mankind. It follows that the new understanding of justice must reach equally far if it is to attest the restoration of man in nature and history to the new and obedient double relatedness of man to God and society. This final possibility of the organization of society into a world community requires most of all that man remember his bond to God and his divinely willed re-instatement in freedom and finiteness, in nature and history. Otherwise this world community will be either a mere phantom of utopian idealists or the worst of all pitfalls, because the destruction into which self-deceived, self-powered man falls, dragging his fellowmen in with him, will be all inclusive.

"Thus we face all the old problems of political organization on the new level of a potential international community. The new international community will be constructed neither by the pessimists, who believe it impossible to go beyond the balance of power principle in the relation of nations to each other; nor by the cynics, who would organize the world by the imposition of imperial authority without regard to the injustices which flow inevitably from arbitrary and irresponsible power; nor yet by the idealists, who are under the fond illusion that a new level of historic development will emancipate history of these vexing problems.

"The new world must be built by resolute men who 'when hope

is dead will hope by faith'; who will neither seek premature escape from the guilt of history, nor yet call the evil, which taints all their achievements, good. There is no escape from the paradoxical relation of history to the Kingdom of God. History moves towards the realization of the Kingdom but yet the judgment of God is upon every new realization."[60]

b) The Transcendent Goal

Niebuhr has affirmed the world-wide possibilities and responsibilities of man, and he has sounded a summons to resolute men who are able to sustain the burden of their task because they hope in faith. He asserts with all possible emphasis that the hope, and the faith, and therefore the possibility of continuing the task depend wholly upon God's installation of these men in their position in natural finite history and historical finitude. They must remain under the tension of the ever-present possibility that they fall again, because of their freedom, into sinful perversion and guilt. Yet this tension has meaning; it is good and ordained by God, because its origin, its centre and its resolving lie in God's turning to man and through man to society.

So once more Niebuhr sets the totality of human history in close relation to the life of the individual in order then to set both in relation to God's redeeming activity above, for and in history. In His creative love, God made man a creature in His own image, fitted for loving in freedom. Man in his obstinate self-seeking tore himself loose from love. The man, so ruined and lost in chaos of his own making, God restored through His redeeming act in Jesus Christ. Finally it is God who in the fulfillment of historical time, in His final judgment and His final redemption ends the confusion and torture of human sin. By and from this end, God gives now faith and trust to the man who surrenders himself to Him. God illuminates history with a meaning given by this end and fulfillment. So God establishes the individual unity of man's being and action, here and now, under the light of this last judgment.

The next question must be: where can we find the man who so hopes and believes. Niebuhr answers by pointing to the church. The church is nothing other than the community of believers. The church is *communio sanctorum* and *congregatio;* here man is brought into the restoring love of God and here he lives in community with his neighbor.

This love of God can so transform man that in repentance and obedience towards God, in humility and brotherliness towards men, he accepts his divinely ordered station in nature and history. His acceptance is personal, willing and free. He knows that the limited possibility given him is needful and meaningful for one who is to be the true mediator in the relatedness of God and society. Here, in the church, faith and society are known as the true poles of man's original state and of his restoration to his close twofold relatedness.

The church is in the world, even if not of the world, and stands therefore under the limitations and dangers of mankind. Yet the church lives from the revelation of the redemptive act of God in Jesus Christ and its consummation in the end of the days where her fulfillment lies. The church therefore is for Niebuhr the truly eschatological community in which the end and goal of all human existence are inherent and are proclaimed. But God's activity in history is not to be confused by the church with her own doing and leaving undone. The church is never the mediator of salvation. The church, no more than society, is in itself the goal of God's concern for men in the sense that it could be itself the final end. Both church and society know their goal to be set by God's redemptive act in the last judgment toward which they look. That this goal may be known, that men in society may from it understand themselves and their relatedness, that society may so become the eschatological community, defines for Niebuhr the task of the church. This goal, which alone justifies the existence of the church, is proclaimed in word and sacrament.

Because the church is so peculiarly the community in which

the will of God should be conspicuously performed, the church herself stands in especial danger. She tries to claim rather than proclaim the bond between God and man. Her danger lies in the continual temptation to believe herself the mediator of salvation and to find her basis in herself and her organization.

The church portrays in her preaching of the Word the true character of the relatedness between God and man, the personal, voluntary love of God's summons and man's obedient and grateful answer. The sacraments of the church witness unequivocally to the paradox of grace in which the community lives by faith and in hope. Partaking in the Agape, the communion of love, "shows forth" love in community. But the church can never claim to have attained this love or to possess it. Her danger is that she may assume herself to be the end of history and the fulfillment of her own purpose; that she may offer as proof of the truth of her message the continuity of her tradition, the "efficacy" of her doctrine, or the powerful appeal of her historical embodiment. She longs to achieve in herself perfection and eternity within history. She lives too little in faith and hope and too much on the presumption of her own righteousness. In short, the church, because she is not sufficiently eschatological, is always in danger of becoming an anti-Christ.

For Niebuhr therefore the stress in the message of the church must be upon eschatology if the totality of the gospel message is not to be compressed or otherwise distorted. Certainly a "gospel," a "message of joy," which affirms the dread last judgment without the proclamation of the redemptive act of God, preceding and conditioning it, is an impossible contradiction. The church, and with her every individual believer, must keep eyes fixed steadfastly on the goal of fulfillment, for in that goal is found the criterion for the message of the church to society.

Niebuhr therefore turns next to consider the eschatological goal of all existence. He sees life and event burdened by the alternatives of end as goal and end as extermination, for which he uses the terms *telos* and *finis*. Man alone, among the creatures, is burdened by the knowledge that all which exists is moving ceaselessly toward a destructive and disintegrating end. This oppresses him especially because the end as *finis,* a sudden, incalculable cutting off of existence, thwarts the achievement of the goal, of *telos,* makes it doubtful if not impossible. By *finis,* the sinful desire of man to make himself secure, to fulfil, eternalize and deify himself, is most obviously menaced with the loss of hope and of all meaning. Death especially so threatens it. Death is the wages of sin, and death is the proof that man cannot give to himself meaning, goal and fulfillment.

It is then necessary to look at the end and goal which God has set for the individual and for all history, since this goal puts the meaning of death in a different light. We are reminded of what has already been emphasized, that this transcendent goal has given direction to all human existence in history and promises the fulfillment of that existence. But the fulfillment means judgment when our relatedness to God is fulfilled and judgment is pronounced over our relatedness to our fellowmen. That judgment will declare whether our relation to our fellowmen has been the bond of brotherhood, without limit and without selfish aim; whether it has spread abroad the love of Christ and has served Christ Himself in serving other men, according to the word of Matthew's Gospel in chapter 25:40. What Niebuhr most desires is that this eschatological message of the New Testament may reach us anew and give us direction.

But Niebuhr knows very well the difficulty of accepting the New Testament teaching of the end, the Christian eschatology. He is cognizant of the sincere struggle of the church for a right insight into its meaning. But he knows also the retreats of the church in both directions: either to a literal fundamentalist misunderstanding which clings to the temporary and temporally conditioned letter; or to the liberal over-confidence which, seeing everything as time-conditioned, discounts eschatology, and because of its unquestioning trust in progress believes that all eschatology can easily be discarded. Niebuhr has observed also all the enthusiastic sects which imagine eschatology, especially its apocalyptic portions, to be an exact diagram of history and the final judgment, a usable gadget for their own household of faith, which they conceive not as God's wisdom and His judgment upon them, but as a private spyglass into God's secrets.

Niebuhr strives to free the message of eschatology from all the mis-interpretations which have obscured it, and to make plain its true meaning and significance. He uses for this purpose *in concreto* his understanding of myth, and in his discussion gives us together with his enlightening statements upon New Testament eschatology an implicit and valuable clarification of his conception of hermeneutics.

The content of Biblical eschatology Niebuhr finds embodied in three symbols (as he calls them): the Second Coming of Christ, the Last Judgment and the Resurrection. In the Second Coming of Christ, he sees primarily the guarantee for man's hope and trust in God in the midst of history which so often mocks his faith. The Second Coming makes clear God's sovereignty over history and even more His purpose to work on and in history. Christ comes again to this earth where in the eyes of the secular historian he suffered total defeat in his earthly life. Further, He returns to this earth which apart from Him cannot fulfil itself and on which, because of man's self-willed and self-glorifying attempts at historical fulfillment, those who believe in Him must accept suffering and persecution.

Upon this follows the meaning of the Last Judgment which does not annul good and evil, but for the first time gives proof that "good" means the fulfilling of the will of God with all our might and our full possibility, and in this world; that evil consists in the misuse of our capacities for our own fulfilment against the will of God and consequently also against our fellowmen. The meaning of human existence as ordained by God in the creation is wholly and finally revealed. The judgment is not upon the amount of human achievement or lack of achievement, but upon man's willingness or unwillingness to allow all of himself to be incorporated into the loving, redeeming will of God and into the service of his neighbor. The mercy of God in the last judgment means that the being and action of man when he is bound to the life-giving God are life-saving and accepted by God; man's self-will which destroys life and community is damned.

It is the Resurrection—the Resurrection of the Body, as the Apostles' Creed puts it—which attests that the final judgment is not concerned with moral distinctions in human faults, but with the man himself, in his total personal being. The Resurrection of the Body gives the historical existence of men earnest and determinative reality. At the same time it declares that the love of the personal God encompasses every man in his individuality and freedom; that the *I* of God summons the *Thou* of each man to answer before Him.

The end, *telos*, of history, so understood, reveals the meaning of history, for this end of history is also its fulfillment. All which is said about history—especially what is said theologically—must be consistent with this perspective. But such a perspective, Niebuhr asserts explicitly, can be found only in faith. Faith, which is man's unforced inner bond with God, binds together also eternity, God's being, with time, the domain of human temporality.

"The eternal is the ground and source of the temporal. The divine consciousness gives meaning to the mere succession of natural events by comprehending them simultaneously, even as human consciousness gives meaning to segments of natural sequence by comprehending them simultaneously in memory and foresight.

"Eternity stands at the end of time in the sense that the temporal process cannot be conceived without a *finis;* and eternity cannot be conceived as having a *finis.*" [61]

So in faith man's freedom is bound to God and can attain its true measure of greatness. Man's desire for self-glorifying self-deification in history with the resultant blood and woe can be set at naught, for history is seen *sub specie aeternitate*, under God who in Jesus Christ stooped to the dust of the earth even in the death on the cross, in order that man might not be lost, but that the mighty should be put down from their seats and they of low degree be exalted. In faith man knows that this God does not in His anger annihilate history, however torn and distorted it be by human pride and the human struggle for power. He wills not the death of the sinner, but rather that he return and live. And man can also comprehend that this life-giving love of God makes possible, preserves and shall fulfil all temporary and finite life. Therefore in faith, man will view historical time not merely as the negative of eternity, but also as the realm where suffering love conquers in secret and where wheat grows among the tares. He will be both more humble and more cautious. In faith man's freedom binds itself willingly to his finiteness in order that the whole man in his God-created unity may serve the eternal.

In the rise and fall of civilization and cultures, the believer recognizes the bond of the life of the individual to nature and to mankind's decisions and mistakes. The unity of history is given by the eternal love of God. Its incongruities and multiplicities witness to the freedom of man, to his possibility and his responsibility, to his guilty disintegration and disintegrating. History in its unity and variety witnesses to man's new hope and his true reality in the restoration through the love of God which rescues and preserves him, which binds him and relates him to his brother. Only if history is considered simultaneously both from the disordered variety of its phenomena and from its single directing final fulfillment, can its variety and its unity be justly evaluated in their mutually conditioning relation. Only a history which is understood from the Creator who ordered it, the Redeemer who restores it and the Saviour who fulfils it, a history seen in living relation to God, can appear to man as meaningful in its nature and destiny.

We are thus led to the conviction that history is ruled *providentia dei et confusione hominum*, by the Providence of God and the disorder of men. The recognition of this truth by repentant man, confessing his sins before God and fellowmen, is truly man's highest achievement. But this confession is not the last word. The last word is said, specifically to the repentant sinner, in God's gracious acceptance and fulfillment of man's being so that finally God becomes all in all. This word can be received only by an obedient faith which is the loving answer to God's personal turning to men. Here all thinking and speaking—even theological dogmas and doctrines—must cease. Here the eternal loving will of God in inner communion with men reaches like a mighty rainbow from the beginning of the world to its end, proclaiming, like the sign of promise given to Noah, the peace of God and His good will to men.

Conclusion

We have still to bring together what has been included in this book and to consider its significance as a whole. Such a recapitulation is the more necessary because in the foregoing presentation Niebuhr's thought appears at first sight somewhat unfamiliar and unusual for a theologian. Just what is the nature of this singularity? The first element certainly is that Niebuhr is a strictly analytical thinker. He starts from the given facts and searches out the causes and the relations of these facts. The man of the first half of the twentieth century stands before Niebuhr's keen eyes and acute intelligence in his total lack of counsel and direction, in the confused and confusing complex of his conception of world and humanity, and under the threatening danger of losing his own identity and his true personality. Many years ago in Detroit Niebuhr met the crucial and particular problem of the modern man.

Niebuhr had believed himself well prepared for the encounter with human problems. The task which took him to Detroit was the acceptance of a pastorate. In preparation he had had a good liberal arts education at Elmhurst College, and had zealously pursued his theological study at the Divinity School of Yale University. The latter gave him excellent training in the liberal theology of the American brand dominant there.

The years in Detroit proved him to be not only a brilliant preacher and trusted pastor, but also an especially gifted writer and speaker. But they brought him also double and bitter disappointment. Simultaneously and in similar fashion he was forced to admit that neither the theology nor the conception of man which he had been taught could be made to correspond with the reality which he was now experiencing. Both were extraneous to that reality and gave no aid toward comprehending it. Both left the young pastor floundering helplessly. The message which he had to proclaim seemed to him without cogency or pertinence for the men of his church whom he did not really understand and who could not feel themselves understood by him. Gospel and world seemed no longer in contact; all relation between them had apparently been lost.

Or was the truth that the preaching of the gospel had been diluted, been made ineffective and become savorless salt? And was the reality of the world perhaps wholly different from what Niebuhr had been taught to see? Different also from what the world itself desired to show? What is the true content of the gospel which still has something to say to present day man? And on the other side what is the essential and special character of man and his world to which the gospel must speak?

This twofold question constitutes the central problem of all Niebuhr's work. Finding the answer became the prime necessity of his own existence to the young preacher of the gospel to the world of his time. For how could he in honor remain in the ministry, if gospel and world could not be brought together? Nor did his professorial appointment lessen the compulsion to search for the solution. The relation of gospel and world is the fixed centre of his thinking around which the whole continually turns. From this point all areas of life, near and far, are subjected to the spot-light of his keen observation. But however far the searchlight beam of his investigation may extend in both directions, into theology and into human existence, the centre remains the same. However much Niebuhr's views may alter, here lies the immovable fixed point by which their acceptance or rejection is ultimately decided.

The task to which Niebuhr knew himself called was to ascertain and trace out the connection between gospel and world. The hypothesis for his work was that the true nature of both and of their mutual relationship would be made clear by this connection. His tool was the acute and meticulous analysis to which he ruthlessly subjected both theology as it was known to him through his study and the world as it now presented itself to him.

The method which he chose as congruous with the apparent contradiction between gospel and world was the dialectic. For him both the justification of dialectic and its definite limitations lay in this apparent contradiction. Niebuhr, as a dialectic thinker, is profoundly convinced that all existence becomes meaningless if the contradiction between gospel and world is inherent and absolute. Therefore he seeks desperately for their original correlation. For him the threat of meaninglessness has become so terrifyingly clear in the human wreckage of the present time that he can tolerate no sort of blurring or minimizing because truth may literally thereby be arrested in untruth. His persistent honesty combined with Anglo-Saxon realism led him toward the theological movement which because of a similar experience and the same refusal to compromise had forced a theological revival on the European continent—even though the point of attack of the dialectic theology was different from his own.

In addition to his keen intellect and his untiring avidity for knowledge, Neibuhr had another gift of value for his analysis—the absolute lack of pre-judgment with which he approached all his problems. It is plain that the manifestly broken relation between gospel and world with which he found himself confronted was not something which he had previously been taught and which he had accepted. Nor was it a problem of disharmony easily soluble by attributing blame to one only of the two factors in the relation. Niebuhr always determinedly considered both gospel and world in his search for the causes of the break and for possible aids to restoration. His sincerity and inability to compromise gave him continually a fresh impulse to probe ever more deeply in his analysis to learn whether he had been led by his new insights to the real heart of the problem; whether the tentative explanations and the methods of inquiry which offered themselves were suited to find the most deeply seated and fundamental causes of the break in the relation between gospel and world.

We find especially in Niebuhr's early work a clear development toward ever greater radicalism. He may have begun by hoping that the causes of the disconnection lay in small awkwardnesses and lacks of proportion within theology, and slight defects of insight, easily remedied by better teaching, on the side of the world. But he became ever more certain that all the theological inconsistencies and all the multiple dislocations and miseries in human society are simply effects, arising from the sole and grievous cause of earth's chaos—the cause in man himself. It is not the disjoined relation between gospel and world which is the cause of man's confusion in his world environment; the relation of the individual to both gospel and world is perverted because man is perverted in himself. And Niebuhr is equally convinced that this perversion of man's self can be righted only within man's relatedness to gospel and world.

The inner disorder of the individual can never remain restricted to him alone. It spreads out to include both man's religious conceptions and his view of his fellowmen. Niebuhr was forced to the discovery that theology, both liberal and orthodox, misunderstands itself and finds itself in the wrong, because it is involved in the vortex of human confusion, and itself leads to confusion.

Still less is immunity from human disorder possible for religion, which Niebuhr sees functioning as a human endeavor to assume without let or hindrance the bond with God in order to extract easily from it the necessary premises for ethical relations in society. The reality is very different. Religion is not at man's disposal, and whenever man has attempted so to use it, it has lost its force and its directing power, and sunk into a cheap and unworkable gadget of human self-satisfaction.

But the world also did not seem to know its difficulties at all fully and showed no desire to admit them or be rid of them. On the contrary, every one appeared to believe that anything which might be wrong was merely the result of external circumstances which could be removed without difficulty as simply as they had arisen. The world as a whole was developing inevitably, in conformity with its own laws and with no possibility of obstruction, towards greater and greater completeness, and was therefore essentially in order. Niebuhr found men as convinced of this as they were of the fact that no individual could be held responsible for the existing problems; the individual was only the sufferer from them.

We can neither comprehend Niebuhr's keen and penetrating analyses in the area of human religion and culture, in man's social, economic and political life, nor understand why they were ever made, if we do not realize Niebuhr's own horror at the baselessness and erroneousness of the views which he had until then unthinkingly shared with his contemporaries. These contemporaries now showed themselves totally unwilling to be shaken out of such views, and Niebuhr was forced to suppose that he had not yet found the right point of attack on the problem of the unique human situation.

Especially important in this phase of his development were the writings of the dialectical theologians who were beginning to give a wholesome shock to the theology of the continent. The starting point of the new theology was entirely different from Niebuhr's. It began with a new understanding of the Word of God and the absolute validity of the message from the One Sovereign God, who in His self-humbling in Jesus Christ disclosed His unconditioned, irresistible Lordship of grace.

This theological movement influenced Niebuhr most deeply through its chief exponents, Karl Barth and Emil Brunner. Niebuhr recognized that Barth's concepts and the whole direction of his thinking had inspired an epochal renewal in theology. But he himself was influenced far more by the writings of Emil Brunner who came much closer to his own problems. Brunner from his new understanding of the scripture was able to discuss not only with theologians but also with men in the secular world. And he was able to convince the latter that the message of the Bible was both comprehensible and applicable to the modern world. Niebuhr found in Brunner's work both promise and guidance for his own task.

Niebuhr met the challenge of this dialectic theology as he had before dealt with the fathers of the church, especially Augustine and the leaders of the Reformation. He did not lose sight of the goal of his own work; rather he was confirmed in his own purpose by the new insight he received and the attainment of his goal became still more imperative.

If it is true that it is God Himself who discloses in His revelation the original state of man and man's true nature as dependent on the personal voluntary relatedness between God and man; if in reality the faith of man which accepts this Only God and affirms this divine revelation is in itself a validated act and does not arise out of man's own nature; then religion, as Niebuhr had formerly understood it, has no function. Revelation and faith constitute the only bonds in the relatedness between God and man. Then the confusion at the centre of man's being, with all its consequences as Niebuhr had known them, is shown to be the exact opposite of this faith. It is man's definite and voluntary denial, man's unbelief, or as Niebuhr from now on always names it, man's sin. The Biblical teaching on sin, indeed, coincides fully with what Niebuhr had observed as the nature and consequence of man's perversion in his relatedness to God and to his fellowmen. At this point in Niebuhr's thinking a decisive reversal began which continued in *Beyond Tragedy* and later was developed more fully in *Nature and Destiny of Man* and in *Faith and History*.

Niebuhr's own fundamental concern, the relation between gospel and world, had been forcefully presented from the point of view of the gospel by the dialectical theologians. His own analyses had been freshly confirmed and were perhaps given a deeper significance. In fact, the content of the dialectic theology basically undergirded Niebuhr's own, and left him free for the work imposed upon him by his position as Professor of Applied Christianity, and by his own special abilities. His work was to develop fully the application of these insights to the nature and the situation of man and of the world as a whole.

Niebuhr's theology had demonstrated that we are not of the world but have our origin in the life-giving love of God. And Niebuhr knows that precisely this insight makes a special demand upon us because, since we still are actually in the world, the truth of the insight must be proved in the world. This proof must be threefold:

First, the restoration of man through the will of God and the acceptance of this restoration in man's faith must create a new sense of fellowship in society, must create a brotherliness in which society itself will become true community.

Second, man's understanding of the world and of himself in history must become new, so that he comprehends afresh their meaning and goal.

Third, there follows for the Christian the necessity of seriously opposing and combatting the secular view of the world and history, because that view is partly the cause and partly the result of the sinful perversion of modern man.

Even though these three requirements are not clearly distinguished and separated in Niebuhr's work, it is fair to say that the first dominates his earlier books and corresponds to the demands of his social analysis, while the other two gain more and more importance in his later books.

The change in Niebuhr's understanding of history had several causes, inner and external. The dialectic theology had made him increasingly attentive to the meaning of the Bible, and in consequence the problem of history became more urgent. The message of the Bible revealed the will of God for the salvation of historical men; its complete revelation declared that God Himself, for the rescue of men in history, became Himself in His Son an historical person. Toward this event the prophets of the Old Testament point. To it the community of the New Testament bears witness.

In the original order of creation, God made possible, by the unique position accorded to man, a history within which man can make free decisions and where, in contrast to naturally determined happenings, there is responsibility. In a different sense, men in their limited self-transcendence, by remembering, surveying and recording, create that which we call history.

But God is always the actuating force in history. He interprets its events and charts its course through the word of His prophets; He enters it Himself in Christ. At the end of the days, He has set a goal for history toward which it is striving and from which it today receives its meaning and direction. The restoration of men requires a new view of history, defined by the interpretation of history in the New Testament. Therefore Niebuhr demands of a true theology not only that it make the Biblical message comprehensible to man in his present temporal situation, but also that it convince him that his place in history has a meaning which is God-given and therefore good; that his individual history finds its meaning in the total meaning of the history ruled by God, and its goal in God's final judgment.

Niebuhr then was forced to formulate his radical disagreement with non-Christian conceptions of history. In his understanding of history (as in his whole theological systematization) he has been much influenced by his former colleague on the Union Faculty, the theologian Paul Tillich, and he has also depended on the work of his brother, H. Richard Niebuhr, Professor of Theology and Christian Ethics at Yale Divinity School. Like them, he condemns especially the modern optimistic interpretation of history. This optimism seems to him exceedingly dangerous, because it is not consistent with historical facts and does not meet honestly and adequately the tasks which these facts impose upon us. It derives from a specific view of history as determined by natural law. The Greeks, who accepted this determinism by nature, considered history therefore to be without meaning. But under the influence of Naturalism, this same determinism now appears as the guarantor of the meaning of history, and of its fulfillment; history's own laws ensure that final and valid and complete fulfillment. It is Niebuhr's special service that in his two major works he has undertaken to controvert the non-Christian systems.

In *Faith and History*, to which he gave the explanatory subtitle "A Comparison of Christian and Modern Views of History," Niebuhr presents systematically the differences between the Christian understanding of history and the modern, a contrast which was noted only incidentally in his earlier work. In a later book, *The Irony of American History*, he applies the insights he has gained particularly to the interpretation which Americans currently make of their own history with its dangerous consequences for the position which the United States has won in the latest world developments. The need for this work (with which we cannot concern ourselves further because it lies outside the framework of Niebuhr's theological works) and the importance of the truth which it presents are best measured by its disconcerting effect in the United States and the kind of arguments by which it has been partially repudiated.[1]

If we try to state in a few words the reason for the importance of Reinhold Niebuhr and his revolutionizing work, we can say with assurance that Niebuhr has investigated with his keen analysis the actuality of modern man; in that investigation he was confronted by the necessity of giving to theology a new direction. He came to see that a new understanding of sin, of revelation and of history was required. But what especially differentiates Niebuhr from his contemporaries among theologians is his refusal to consider the individual as existing in isolation. He sees man always in relatedness to his fellowmen, in a relatedness meaningful as created by God and again to be made fruitful through God's restoration of man. Man's true nature has its foundation in its bond with God and works out its destiny in the fellowship of society.

Niebuhr's theology, in contrast to the continental European, could fairly be called analytic. The former deserves the label synthetic since it starts wholly and exclusively from God's revelation in His Word and in the light of that revelation examines every area of man's life in order to see the whole comprehended in the message of the Bible. In the application of the Christian gospel to the areas of life which apparently have only secular significance, the work of Emil Brunner makes the most important contribution, and it is not surprising that there is close contact between him and Reinhold Niebuhr.

But a European reader of Niebuhr's work may perhaps ask himself, does not Niebuhr's analytic theology imply that a man who is willing to make an honest and thorough analysis of reality must inevitably and indubitably discover Jesus Christ as Saviour and Redeemer, since all that is needed is to find the positive opposite of the negative illusions which are the result of humanity's effort to escape its aimless confusion? Does this not render superfluous in the end the revelation of God and especially an exclusive revelation?

Our presentation of Niebuhr's thought should have made it clear that Niebuhr never so believed, and since his fundamental aim was to uncover the true relatedness of gospel and world he could never so believe. But this charge is important because by considering it and refuting it important distinctions become clear.

First of all, the improbability of such a discovery is evident from the fact that to our knowledge no one has ever found Christ and come to Him by an analytical path. On the contrary, secular, non-Christian analysis of the present situation results either in unfruitful pessimism or unfounded optimism, or perhaps in the deadening cynical resignation which can attach to either. It certainly does not lead to an encounter with Christ. Niebuhr is himself a convincing argument. He did not come and does not claim to have come to Christ by the aid of any analysis. In fact he emphasizes the necessity of the Christian revelation as the only basis for true analysis. He has sought to show from the history of thought that only men with a living faith in the self-revealing God, men like Augustine, were capable of really penetrating and useful analyses of their own times.

There is another and presumably decisive theological confutation which appears in the inner logic of Niebuhr's thinking. There is a mighty and unbridgeable chasm between a negative, intellectual analytical conclusion concerning the necessity of a Christ and the encounter with the living Jesus Christ who reveals Himself and meets each one of us personally in the Holy Spirit. This encounter is possible only in faith which involves the whole person (not the intellect alone) in the voluntary acceptance of this specific and personal Jesus of Nazareth who is the Christ of the world.

Niebuhr says:

"It is not possible to interpret cultures according to their expectation or want of expectations of *a* Christ without drawing upon the faith that *the* Christ has been revealed; for there can be no interpretation of the meaning of life and history without implicitly or explicitly drawing into the interpretation the faith which claims to have found the end of these expectations." [2]

"The fact that there can be no Christ without an expectation of Christ relates Christianity as founded in a unique revelation to the whole history of culture; the fact that the true Christ cannot be the Messiah who is expected separates Christianity from the history of culture." [3]

We must attend closely to Niebuhr's words here. He says plainly that without the expectation of a Christ there can be no Christ. He therefore assumes that this expectation is itself already a part of God's redemptive act in behalf of men who do not yet know Him. The connection is explicitly asserted and this assertion means not only that in general without the expectation of a Christ, all possibility of Christ is precluded; but also, and most significantly for Niebuhr's thinking, the individual who expects no Christ can have neither a living encounter nor any relation whatever with the actual Jesus Christ or with any Christ.

We may here mention a supporting consideration which, however, has nothing to do with the preceding charge against Niebuhr's analytical theology. Niebuhr stresses the fact that the passionate Messianic hopes born from the analytically known oppression of post-exilic Judaism had no place for the Christ revealed in Jesus of Nazareth and resulted in angry repudiation of Him; and he draws the conclusion that an analytically determined adherence to Christ is impossible.

The natural limits of an analytical theology have become clear, as Niebuhr himself has stated them and as he has observed them in his own work. Analytical theology absolutely requires the accompanying and consummating complement of the synthetic; even as the synthetic, without a full application of analysis to man in his present limitation and to the problems which beset him, must remain incomplete. Does the power of Jesus' preaching perhaps lie in the perfect balance between his authority as Revealer and his love reaching out to men in their individuality and finite transitoriness?

In any case, if European theology thinks to repudiate the analytic, and American theology the synthetic method; neither in so doing can avoid incompleteness and consequent unfruitfulness. A neutral observer has recently found such a deficiency in the American churches and considers it the cause of the confusion in religion in America. It is worth noting that he gave his article the title "America on the Hunt for God." [4]

We are confronted with the necessity for a genuine ecumenical theology. It is certainly a sign of promise that without fanfare a piece of genuinely ecumenical work has already been accomplished. Perhaps ecumenicity comes less through great conferences than through God-related men, able to work together in brotherly love and freed by that love from the urge to insist exclusively upon their own particular theological discoveries.

Ecumenical theology has its foundation in the Lord of the church and the world, and in his will that succor be given to all the world. Ecumenical theology is not simply a repository for certain theological postulates or for separate theological disciplines; its concern is the basis and the goal of all theology. Acceptance of this imperative task must lead to sincere and unreserved sharing between separate theological movements. Each must honestly surrender, not its pursuit of truth, but its self-glorifying pride of possession of the truth, in order that all may acknowledge the truth in Christ.

At the level of ecumenical theology, synthetic and analytic theology must work together at their common task. The nature and destiny of the world in God's plan can be rightly known only from the will of God revealed in the Holy Scripture. But the quest demands precisely the analytic theology which is seriously and lovingly concerned with the peculiar nature and complexity of humanity and consequently investigates tirelessly all the questions which trouble men in the world. Fittingly, many of Niebuhr's students are now searching for such an amalgamation of divers theological movements and are earnestly desirous of cooperation with continental theology. (So especially, among others, Professor Paul Lehmann of Princeton Seminary whose work unfortunately is not yet published.)

Niebuhr must always be a much needed stimulus for American theologians and for those in Europe also, since he prevents us from being content with hasty and inadequate answers to the world's crucial questions. His sober look at reality must always occasion a salutary discomfort. He forces the church to face constantly an examination, set by men in the world, upon her message and its true import. Notably he brings together for serious debate theology and the modern man who is outside the church. In America his influence is perhaps greater among non-theologians than with the leaders and preachers of the church. He himself stands always at the meeting place of church and world.

But this position on which Niebuhr insists and which is to make it possible for us to find our own way in theology raises certain questions. Is this position between church and world really a place where we can stand fast? Niebuhr himself once said [5] that his whole theology was really only the unfolding of the meaning of *Christus pro et in nobis,* Christ for and in us, to men in the world. Although this theme may not always be clearly heard throughout the whole of his theology, we have no reason to doubt his purpose. But does not its accomplishment require a much fuller interpretation of the doctrine of the Holy Spirit?

The Holy Spirit is God's complete, personal turning to each one of us in order to promise him personally redemption through Christ and to create in him the work of "becoming new." Niebuhr, who pondered so earnestly the meaning of God, the Father and the Son, seems to have found a difficulty in the person of the Holy Spirit. He could not see how to relate the Holy Spirit to his emphasis on "the second Adam" and the "being in Christ." But how can the "being in Christ" be conceivable without an understanding of the doctrine of the Holy Spirit? In interpreting the "being in Christ," should not the Johannine theology be much more strongly stressed than it is in Niebuhr's work? Also does not much more need to be said and said more definitively about the church? Certainly a much fuller criticism of the church is needed.

But all these further questions which present themselves have their root in the first question: whether we stand or can remain standing so exactly between gospel and world as Niebuhr wishes us to do. The "second Adam" at least does not stand there. We concede to Niebuhr that he is right in his judgment that the majority of theologians stand unconcernedly on one side without even seeing the other. And if a position between gospel and world is not a real possibility, if the real bond uniting gospel to world is always the act of the divine Spirit of love working through us, Niebuhr would certainly choose to stand on the side of the seeking child of the world rather than on the side of the "full" man of the church. But are we so free to choose our station?

Sin is Niebuhr's central concern. This centrality is justified by his original pragmatic recognition of the contradiction between gospel and world and his analytical, dialectic procedure based thereon. Consistently he finds repentance, humility and reinstatement to be the essential marks of the "new man." But we may ask whether with a less arbitrary exegesis of the text of the New Testament a very much more positive picture of the "new man" would not be possible. The question of the validity of Niebuhr's hermeneutics reaches to the very centre of his theology.

Some American critics of Niebuhr have blamed him as a defeatist and pessimist. That verdict is certainly wrong, but the fact that such an impression could arise at all deserves consideration. Have the men who so judge Niebuhr failed to hear correctly what he has said, most positively and in full accord with the gospel, of the victory which overcomes the world? Why have they not listened?

Niebuhr is a pessimist in his judgment of man's own capacity to redeem and perfect himself. Here he sees nothing but black and he can see only black. He appears a defeatist only in opposition to the belief that the world and mankind will finally be able of themselves to pull themselves out of their misery, even supposing that everything does not always come out right by itself. The domination of sin shows itself especially in this blindness which can result only in total destruction; here Niebuhr sees the only help in repentance and humility. He is a pessimist only in opposition to a false optimism.

But the Christian insight is not limited to these alternatives. The good news of the gospel rises far above both, in the light of the cross and the Resurrection. What is pessimism before the cross and optimism before the Resurrection?

In Niebuhr's books there rings out an imperative protest against the attitude characteristic of many American preachers, who apparently reflect and learnedly expatiate upon gospel and world in order either to combine them for their own profit or to set them forever apart in total opposition. They seek to dominate gospel and world, and so reject their calling as obedient and wise servants of God's Word, to whom the practice of an insipid moral pedagoguery upon their fellowmen is forbidden by the love of Christ, which alone can bind men to this service.

America is on the hunt for God. Niebuhr has tried by honest and serious analysis to survey and comprehend this search in order that he may announce to the hunters that God Himself has already long ago taken upon Himself the hunt for lost men. We could not seek, if we had not long ago been found by God. God Himself comes to men and our faith can be the thankful affirmation and realization of this bond through our community with our fellowmen in society.

Confessing this truth, we shall be Niebuhr's best pupils if answers for the questions he has left open become our aim in our own theological thinking. To such this book is offered.

NOTES

CHAPTER II

1. von Harnack, Adolf, *Das Wesen des Christentums.* (Translated under the title, *What is Christianity?*)
2. *Leaves from the Notebook of a Tamed Cynic*, Hamden, Conn.: Shoe String Press, p. 27.
3. *Cf.* Carnell, Edward John, *The Concept of Dialectic in the Theology of Reinhold Niebuhr*, Cambridge: Harvard Divinity School, 1948.
4. *Ibid.*, pp. 385ff.
5. Barth, Karl, *Der Römerbrief* (2nd ed.), Munich, 1922. (Translated under the title, *Epistle to the Romans*, New York: Oxford University Press, 1933.)
6. "Coherence, Incoherence and Christian Faith," *The Journal of Religion*, Vol. XXXI, p. 3.
7. "Ten Years That Shook My World." Reprinted by permission of *The Christian Century*, from the issue of April 26, 1939, Vol. LVI/1, No. 17, p. 545.

CHAPTER III

1. *Does Civilization Need Religion? A Study in the Social Resources and Limitations of Religion in Modern Life*, New York: The Macmillan Company, 1928. Used by permission of the publisher.
2. *Ibid.*, pp. 2f.
3. *Ibid.*, p. 4.
4. *Ibid.*, pp. 4f.
5. *Ibid.*, p. 6.
6. *Ibid.*, pp. 6f.
7. *Ibid.*, p. 7
8. *Ibid.*, p. 7
9. *Ibid.*, p. 12
10. *Ibid.*, pp. 22f.
11. *Ibid.*, pp. 23f.
12. *Ibid.*, p. 32
13. *Ibid.*, p. 37
14. *Ibid.*, p. 39
15. *Ibid.*, p. 43
16. *Ibid.*, p. 51

17. *Ibid.*, p. 55
18. *Ibid.*, pp. 63f.
19. *Ibid.*, p. 76
20. *Ibid.*, p. 79
21. *Ibid.*, pp. 80f.
22. *Ibid.*, p. 128
23. *Ibid.*, p. 133
24. *Ibid.*, p. 129
25. *Ibid.*, pp. 165–167
26. *Ibid.*, p. 185
27. *Ibid.*, p. 186
28. *Ibid.*, p. 194
29. *Ibid.*, p. 195
30. *Ibid.*, pp. 196f.
31. *Ibid.*, p. 198
32. *Ibid.*, pp. 199f.
33. *Ibid.*, p. 206
34. *Ibid.*, p. 216
35. "Ten Years That Shook My World." Reprinted by permission of *The Christian Century*, from the issue of April 26, 1939, Vol. LVI/1, No. 17, p. 542.
36. *Moral Man and Immoral Society: A Study in Ethics and Politics*, New York: Charles Scribner's Sons, 1932.
37. *Ibid.*, pp. xif.
38. *Ibid.*, p. xx
39. *Ibid.*, p. 1
40. *Ibid.*, p. 3
41. *Ibid.*, p. 6
42. Cf. Brunner, H. E., *Coercive Power: A Study in American Protestant Ethics Between the Opening of the Twentieth Century and the Second World War*, New York: Union Theological Seminary, 1947, esp. pp. 177ff.
43. *Moral Man and Immoral Society*, p. 11
44. *Ibid.*, pp. 25f.
45. *Ibid.*, p. 27
46. *Ibid.*, pp. 40–42
47. *Ibid.*, pp. 51f.
48. *Ibid.*, p. 112
49. *Ibid.*, p. 114
50. *Ibid.*, p. 117
51. *Ibid.*, p. 136
52. *Ibid.*, p. 141
53. *Ibid.*, pp. 144f.
54. *Ibid.*, pp. 155f.
55. *Ibid.*, p. 164
56. *Ibid.*, pp. 167f.
57. *Ibid.*, p. 194
58. *Ibid.*, pp. 198f.
59. *Ibid.*, p. 223
60. *Ibid.*, p. 226

61. *The Contribution of Religion to Social Work.* The Forbes Lectures of the New York School of Social Work. New York: Columbia University Press, 1932.
62. *Ibid.*, pp. 18f.
63. *Ibid.*, p. 19
64. *Ibid.*, pp. 22–23
65. *Ibid.*, p. 24
66. *Ibid.*, pp. 34f.
67. *Ibid.*, p. 39
68. *Ibid.*, p. 66
69. *Ibid.*, pp. 76f.
70. *Ibid.*, pp. 90f.
71. *Ibid.*, pp. 91f.
72. *Ibid.*, p. 94
73. *Ibid.*, p. 93
74. "Ten Years That Shook My World." Reprinted by permission of *The Christian Century*, from the issue of April 26, 1939, Vol. LVI/1, No. 17, p. 546.
75. *Reflections on the End of an Era*, New York: Charles Scribner's Sons, 1934, p. 9.
76. *Ibid.*, pp. 12f.
77. *Ibid.*, p. 14
78. *Ibid.*, p. 16
79. In a personal talk with the author.
80. *Reflections on the End of an Era*, p. 17
81. *Ibid.*, p. 18
82. *Ibid.*, p. 19
83. *Ibid.*, pp. 31f.
84. Bultmann, Rudolf, "Neues Testament und Mythologie, das Problem der Entmythologisierung der neutestamentlichen Verkündigung," pp. 15–53, in *Kerygma und Mythos, ein theologisches Gespräch*, Hamburg: Reich & Heidrich, Evangelischer Verlag, 1948.
85. *Ibid.*, p. 23
86. *Ibid.*, p. 23
87. *Ibid.*, pp. 23f.
88. *Ibid.*, p. 15
89. *Ibid.*, p. 15
90. *Ibid.*, pp. 16f.
91. "existentiell und existential," a distinction for which English apparently has no exact equivalent. (Translator.)
92. "Neues Testament und Mythologie," p. 47
93. *Ibid.*, p. 50
94. *Ibid.*, pp. 50f.
95. *Ibid.*, p. 51
96. A reference to the poem "Kandidat im Pfarrhaus zu Nöddebo," by Wilhelm Busch.
97. "Neues Testament und Mythologie," pp. 18f.
98. *Ibid.*, p. 52
99. *Reflections on the End of an Era*, p. 123
100. *Ibid.*, p. 124

101. *Ibid.*, pp. 126f.
102. *Ibid.*, p. 135
103. *Ibid.*, p. 136
104. *Ibid.*, pp. 294f.

CHAPTER IV

1. *An Interpretation of Christian Ethics*, New York and London: Harper and Brothers, 1935.
2. *Ibid.*, p. 5
3. *Ibid.*, p. 8
4. *Ibid.*, p. 9
5. *Ibid.*, pp. 12f.
6. *Ibid.*, p. 15
7. *Ibid.*, p. 26
8. *Ibid.*, p. 29
9. *Ibid.*, pp. 30f.
10. *Ibid.*, pp. 33f.
11. *Ibid.*, p. 37
12. *Ibid.*, p. 39
13. *Ibid.*, p. 40
14. *Ibid.*, p. 41
15. *Ibid.*, p. 42
16. *Ibid.*, p. 43
17. *Ibid.*, pp. 56f.
18. *Ibid.*, pp. 58f.
19. *Ibid.*, pp. 60f.
20. *Ibid.*, p. 65
21. *Ibid.*, pp. 66f.
22. *Ibid.*, p. 67
23. Thelen, Mary Frances, *Man as Sinner in Contemporary American Realistic Theology*, New York: King's Crown Press, 1946. *Cf.* pp. 63ff.
24. *An Interpretation of Christian Ethics*, pp. 72–74.
25. *Ibid.*, p. 77
26. *Ibid.*, pp. 84f.
27. *Ibid.*, p. 91
28. *Ibid.*, p. 93
29. *Ibid.*, p. 98
30. *Cf.* Brunner, Emil, *Das Gebot und die Ordnungen, Entwurf einer protestantisch-theologischen Ethik* (3rd ed.), Zürich: Zwingli-Verlag, 1939, and *Gerechtigkeit, eine Lehre von den Grundgesetzen der Gesellschaftordnung*, Zürich: Zwingli-Verlag, 1943.
31. Quotations from *Beyond Tragedy: Essays on the Christian Interpretation of History* by Reinhold Niebuhr; copyright 1937 by Charles Scribner's Sons. Reprinted by permission of the publisher.
32. *Ibid.*, pp. ix–xi.
33. *Ibid.*, pp. 5f.
34. *Ibid.*, p. 8
35. *Ibid.*, pp. 17f.
36. *Ibid.*, p. 20
37. *Ibid.*, pp. 28–30

38. *Ibid.*, pp. 44f.
39. *Ibid.*, p. 62
40. *Ibid.*, p. 98
41. *Ibid.*, p. 100
42. *Ibid.*, pp. 104f.
43. *Ibid.*, pp. 165f.
44. *Ibid.*, pp. 167f.
45. *Ibid.*, p. 180
46. *Ibid.*, p. 182
47. *Ibid.*, p. 257
48. *Ibid.*, p. 261
49. *Ibid.*, pp. 265–267
50. *Ibid.*, p. 277
51. *Ibid.*, pp. 292f.
52. *Ibid.*, pp. 294f.
53. *Ibid.*, p. 297
54. *Ibid.*, p. 306

CHAPTER V

1. Quotations from *The Nature and Destiny of Man: A Christian Interpretation* by Reinhold Niebuhr; copyright 1941, 1943 by Charles Scribner's Sons. Reprinted by permission of the publisher.
2. *Faith and History: A Comparison of Christian and Modern Views of History*, New York: Charles Scribner's Sons, 1949.
3. *The Nature and Destiny of Man*, Vol. I, p. 1
4. Kierkegaard, Sören, *The Sickness unto Death* (translated by Walter Lowrie), Princeton: Princeton University Press, 1944.
5. *Cf.* Carnell, Edward J., *The Concept of Dialectic in the Theology of Reinhold Niebuhr*, Cambridge: Harvard Divinity School, 1948.
6. Brunner, Emil, *Der Mensch im Widerspruch, die Christliche Lehre vom Wahren und vom Wirklichen Menschen*, Berlin, 1937. (Translated under the title *Man in Revolt*, Philadelphia: The Westminster Press, 1947.)
7. *The Nature and Destiny of Man*, Vol. I, p. 15
8. *Ibid.*, Vol. I, pp. 126f.
9. *Ibid.*, Vol. I, p. 127
10. *Ibid.*, Vol. I, p. 129
11. *Ibid.*, Vol. I, pp. 131f.
12. *Ibid.*, Vol. I, p. 136
13. *Ibid.*, Vol. I, p. 150
14. *Ibid.*, Vol. I, p. 167
15. *Ibid.*, Vol. I, p. 168
16. *Ibid.*, Vol. I, pp. 169f.
17. *Ibid.*, Vol. I, p. 266
18. *Ibid.*, Vol. I, pp. 269f.
19. *Ibid.*, Vol. I, pp. 270f.
20. *Ibid.*, Vol. I, pp. 271f.
21. *Ibid.*, Vol. I, pp. 277f.
22. *Ibid.*, Vol. I, pp. 279f.
23. *Ibid.*, Vol. I, p. 295

24. *Ibid.*, Vol. I, p. 300
25. *Ibid.*, Vol. I, p. 18
26. *Ibid.*, Vol. I, p. 27
27. *Ibid.*, Vol. I, p. 54
28. *Ibid.*, Vol. I, p. 55
29. *Ibid.*, Vol. I, pp. 30f.
30. *Ibid.*, Vol. I, pp. 39f.
31. *Ibid.*, Vol. I, p. 61
32. *Ibid.*, Vol. I, pp. 65f.
33. *Ibid.*, Vol. I, p. 92
34. *Ibid.*, Vol. I, p. 93
35. *Ibid.*, Vol. I, p. 104
36. *Ibid.*, Vol. I, p. 122
37. *Ibid.*, Vol. I, pp. 178f.
38. *Ibid.*, Vol. I, p. 179
39. *Ibid.*, Vol. I, pp. 179f.
40. *Ibid.*, Vol. I, p. 188
41. *Ibid.*, Vol. I, p. 203
42. *Ibid.*, Vol. I, p. 204
43. *Ibid.*, Vol. I, pp. 208f.
44. *Ibid.*, Vol. I, p. 213
45. *Ibid.*, Vol. I, p. 222
46. *Ibid.*, Vol. I, p. 228
47. *Ibid.*, Vol. I, p. 240
48. *Ibid.*, Vol. I, p. 242
49. *Ibid.*, Vol. II, pp. 1f.
50. *Faith and History*, p. 14
51. *The Nature and Destiny of Man*, Vol. II, p. 16
52. *Ibid.*, Vol. I, pp. 138f.
53. *Ibid.*, Vol. I, pp. 139f.
54. *Ibid.*, Vol. I, p. 140
55. *Ibid.*, Vol. II, p. 38
56. *Cf. ibid.*, Vol. II, pp. 39f.
57. *Ibid.*, Vol. II, p. 43
58. *Ibid.*, Vol. II, p. 243
59. *Ibid.*, Vol. II, p. 284
60. *Ibid.*, Vol. II, pp. 285f.
61. *Ibid.*, Vol. II, p. 299

CONCLUSION

1. *Cf.* West, Anthony, "Night and Fog," in *The New Yorker*, May 3, 1952, pp. 130ff.
2. *The Nature and Destiny of Man*, Vol. II, pp. 5f.
3. *Ibid.*, Vol. II, p. 16
4. *Cf.* Jungk, Robert, "Amerika auf der Suche nach Gott," in *Die Weltwoche*, 20 Jahrgang, No. 5, Dec. 1952, pp. 4f.
5. In a personal conference with the author.

BIBLIOGRAPHY

1. The Works of Reinhold Niebuhr

a. His Books

Does Civilization Need Religion? A Study in the Social Resources and Limitations in Modern Life, The Macmillan Co., New York, 1928

Leaves from the Notebook of a Tamed Cynic, Willett, Clark & Colby, New York, 1929 (now available through Shoe String Press, Hamden, Conn., 1955)

Moral Man and Immoral Society, A Study in Ethics and Politics, Charles Scribner's Sons, New York and London, 1932

The Contribution of Religion to Social Work, published by The New York School of Social Work, Columbia University Press, New York, 1932

Reflections on the End of an Era, Charles Scribner's Sons, New York, 1934

An Interpretation of Christian Ethics, Harper & Brothers, New York, 1935

Do the State and Nation Belong to God or the Devil?, Student Christian Movement Press, London, 1937

Beyond Tragedy, Essays on the Christian Interpretation of History, Charles Scribner's Sons, New York, 1937

Europe's Catastrophe and the Christian Faith, James Nisbet & Co., London, 1940

Christianity and Power Politics, Charles Scribner's Sons, New York, 1940

The Nature and Destiny of Man, A Christian Interpretation (the Gifford Lectures), Charles Scribner's Sons, New York, 1941 & 1943

The Children of Light and the Children of Darkness, A Vindication of Democracy and a Critique of Its Traditional Defence, Charles Scribner's Sons, New York, 1944

Discerning the Signs of the Times, Sermons for Today and Tomorrow, Charles Scribner's Sons, New York, 1946

Faith and History, A Comparison of Christian and Modern Views of History, Charles Scribner's Sons, New York, 1949

The Illusion of World Government, The Graphics Group, Whitestone, New York, 1949

The Irony of American History, Charles Scribner's Sons, New York, 1952

Christian Realism and Political Problems. Essays on Political, Social, Ethical, and Theological Themes, Charles Scribner's Sons, New York, 1953

The Self and the Dramas of History, Charles Scribner's Sons, New York, 1955.

b. Some of His Articles

"The Practical Unbelief of Modern Civilization" in *Religion on the Campus* (The Report of the National Student Conference, Milwaukee), edited by Francis P. Miller, Association Press, New York, 1927, Chapter II, pp. 11ff.

"Christianity and Redemption" in *Whither Christianity?*, edited by Lynn Harold Hough, Harper & Brothers, New York, 1929, Chapter VII, pp. 110ff.

"Christian Faith in the Modern World" in *Ventures in Belief, Christian Convictions for a Day of Uncertainty*, edited by Henry P. Van Dusen, Charles Scribner's Sons, New York, 1929, pp. 5ff.

"Religion and Moral Experience" in *What Religion Means To Me*, by Reinhold Niebuhr, H. E. Fosdick, *et al.*, Doubleday, Doran & Co., New York, 1929, pp. 56ff.

"Protestantism, Capitalism and Communism" in *Religion Today, A Challenging Enigma*, edited by Arthur L. Swift, Jr., Whittlesey House, McGraw-Hill Book Co., New York, 1933, pp. 138ff.

"Don't Preach Ideals in a Vacuum!" in *The American Friend*, Vol. XXIII, No. 11, May 30, 1935, pp. 208f.

"Social Justice" in *Christianity and Communism*, edited by Henry W. Harris, Marshall Jones & Co., Boston, 1937, Chapter V, pp. 62ff.

"Why the Christian Church is Not Pacifist," Student Christian Movement Press, London, 1940

"Nature and Destiny of Man" in *Theology Today*, Vol. I, No. 2, July 1944, p. 236

"Changing and Abiding Elements in the Human Situation," (the first Alexandre H. White Foundation Lectures), in *Current Religious Thought*, Vol. V, No. 6, June 1945, pp. 23ff.

"Theologian and Church Statesman" in *This Ministry, The Contribution of Henry Sloane Coffin*, Charles Scribner's Sons, New York, 1946, pp. 117ff.

"The Relevance of Reformation Doctrine in Our Day" in *The Heritage of the Reformation, Essays Commemo-*

rating the Centennial of Eden Theological Seminary, edited by Elmer J. F. Arndt, Richard R. Smith, New York, 1950, pp. 249ff.

"The Hydrogen Bomb" in *The Messenger*, Vol. XV, No. 5, February 28, 1950, p. 7

"The Second Half of the Century" in *The Messenger*, Vol. XV, No. 2, January 17, 1950, p. 9

"The Grace of Christ" in *The Messenger*, Vol. XV, No. 7, March 28, 1950, p. 6

"Grace and Self-acceptance" in *The Messenger*, Vol. XV, No. 7, April 25, 1950, p. 6

"Law and Grace" in *The Messenger*, Vol. XV, No. 13, June 20, 1950, p. 5

"Christian Faith and Social Action" in *Christian Faith and Social Action*, edited by John A. Hutchison, Charles Scribner's Sons, New York, 1953, pp. 225ff.

2. Works and Articles of Other Authors about Reinhold Niebuhr and His Theology

Allen, E. A.: *Christianity and Society*, *A Guide to the Thought of Reinhold Niebuhr*, Hodder and Stoughton, London, 1949; The Philosophical Library, New York, 1951

Bagby, Grover Carlton: *Human Freedom and Responsibility in the Light of the Writings of Reinhold Niebuhr* (Ph. D. thesis), Drew Theological Seminary, Madison, N. J., 1947

Boume, Howard Arthur: *The Economic Concepts of Emil Brunner and Reinhold Niebuhr* (microfilm dissertation), University of Chicago, 1945

Brunner, H. H.: *Coercive Power, A Study in American Protestant Ethics Between the Opening of the Twentieth Century and the Second World War*, Union Theological Seminary, New York, 1947

Carnell, Edward John: *The Concept of Dialectic in the Theology of Reinhold Niebuhr*, Harvard Divinity School, 1948

Carnell, Edward John: *The Theology of Reinhold Niebuhr*, W. B. Eerdmans Publishing Co., Grand Rapids, Mich., 1951

Davies, D. R.: *Reinhold Niebuhr, Prophet From America*, James Clarke & Co., London, 1945

Davis, H. R.: *The Political Philosophy of Reinhold Niebuhr* (Ph. D. Inaugural Dissertation), University of Chicago, 1951 (mim.)

Eddy, Sherwood: *Man Discovers God*, Harper & Brothers, New York and London, 1942, pp. 211ff.

Hammar, George: "Reinhold Niebuhr's Way from Social Ethics to a Realistic Theology" in *Christian Realism in Contemporary American Theology, A Study of Reinhold Niebuhr, William Horton and H. P. Van Dusen*, A.-B. Lundequistska Bokhandeln, Uppsala, Sweden, 1940

Hough, Lynn Harold: "Niebuhr on the Meaning of History" in *The Pastor*, Vol. XII, No. 11, July 1949, pp. 2ff.

Hutchison, John A. (ed.): *Christian Faith and Social Action*, Charles Scribner's Sons, New York, 1953

Jones, Edgar Dewitt: "Reinhold Niebuhr" in *American Preachers of Today*, Bobbs-Merrill Co., Indianapolis, 1933, pp. 249–253

Kegley, Charles W.; and Bretall, Robert W.: *Reinhold Niebuhr, His Religious, Social and Political Thought*,

Vol. II, The Library of Living Theology, Macmillan, New York, 1955

Keller, Adolf: *Der Weg der dialektischen Theologie durch die kirchlich Welt, Eine kleine Theologiekunde der Gegenwart,* Chr. Kaiser Verlag, Munich, 1931

Keller, Adolf: *Amerikanisches Christentum heute,* Evang. Verlag Zollikon, 1943

Lehmann, Paul L.: "A Watershed in American Theology" in *Theology Today,* Vol. I, No. 2, July 1944, p. 234

Lewis, Hywel David: *Morals and the New Theology,* Harper & Brothers, New York, 1947

Macgregor, G. H. C.: *The Relevance of the Impossible, A Reply to Reinhold Niebuhr,* The Fellowship of Reconciliation, London, 1941

Maier, Anton: *Das Menschenbild Reinhold Niebuhrs, der Mensch in Gemeinschaft und Geschichte* (Ph. D. Inaugural Dissertation), University of Heidelberg, 1954 (mim.)

Muelder, Walter G.: "Reinhold Niebuhr's Conception of Man" in *The Personalist,* Vol. XXVI, No. 3, July 1945, pp. 282–293

Schrey, Heinz-Horst: "Die Wiedergeburt des Naturrechtes" in *Theologische Rundschau,* Neue Folge, 19 Jahrgang, No. 2, September 1951, J. C. B. Mohr, Tubingen, pp. 164ff.

Thelen, Mary Frances: *Man as Sinner in Contemporary American Realistic Theology,* King's Crown Press, New York, 1946

van Till, C.: "Nature and Destiny of Man" in *The Westminster Theological Journal,* Vol. V, Spring 1943, pp. 206ff.

Weichenhan, Otthrecht: *Die sozialethischen Voraussetzungen und Zielsetzungen der Theologie Reinhold Niebuhrs* (Th. D. Inaugural Dissertation), University of Göttingen, 1954 (mim.)

Wieman, Henry N. *et al.*: *Religious Liberals Reply*, The Beacon Press, Boston, 1947

Wieman, Henry N. and Meland, Bernard E.: *American Philosophies of Religion*, Willett, Clark & Co., Chicago and New York, 1936, pp. 94f.

3. Bibliographies

Hinds, Asher E.: *Bibliography of Reinhold Niebuhr*, Princeton, 1942 (mim.)

Kegley, Charles, and Bretall, Robert W.: *Reinhold Niebuhr, His Religious, Social, and Political Thought*, Vol. II of The Library of Living Theology, The Macmillan Co., New York, 1956. *See* Bibliography at close of work.

Robertson, D. B.: *Reinhold Niebuhr's Works: A Bibliography*, The Berea College Press, Berea, Kentucky, 1954

INDEX

INDEX

Biblical References

INDEX